IN SEARCH OF STEAM DONKEYS

Logging Equipment in Oregon

BY MERV JOHNSON

Consolidated Timber Company, Glenwood, Oregon, circa 1940. *Clark Kinsey photograph from the Lee Lockett Collection*

IN SEARCH OF STEAM DONKEYS

Logging Equipment in Oregon

BY MERV JOHNSON

IN SEARCH OF STEAM DONKEYS

Logging Equipment in Oregon

FIRST EDITION published in 1996

Second Printing, 2002

Published by

P.O. Box 219
Hillsboro, OR 97123

Edited by Philip Schnell

Design and typography by TimberTimes, Inc.

Cover design by Jeanne E. Galick

Manufactured in the United States of America

ISBN   0-9650213-0-0

Library of Congress Control Number: 95-62398

Cover painting   "Manary Logging Co., Camp 12," by Ken Brauner

This scene shows two Willamette steam donkeys at work near Manary Logging Company's Camp 12. A 13x14 high-speed skyline yarder is on the left and a 10x11 loader on the right. Water for these donkeys at this logging site was brought in by tank car and pumped into the large reservoirs by a steam-operated pump with energy supplied by a steam locomotive.

All railroad and logging operations of the Pacific Spruce Corporation of Toledo, Oregon in the 1920s and early 30s were handled by their subsidiary company, the Manary Logging Company. Their network of railroads covered much of the mid-Oregon Coast Range mountains to the Pacific Ocean. Manary Logging Company owned and operated Baldwin, Lima Shay and Porter steam locomotives. (Text by Ken Brauner)

Endpapers   *Unidentified location entitled "Aerial Logging."*
              Weister photo, John T. Labbe Collection

REMNANTS OF THE STEAM LOGGING ERA IN WESTERN OREGON

This work is of interest to historians, modelers, machinery buyers, sellers, and collectors, curiosity seekers, loggers, and lovers of our Pacific Northwest steam logging heritage.

Merv Johnson

A scene the likes of which we will never see again, new steam donkeys being prepared for service in the woods, at The Whitney Company in Idaville, Oregon. A reversal of this scene occurred with the donkeys of Consolidated Timber Co. at the end of their operations in the mid-forties, which coincided with the demise of steam. The donkeys were hauled to yards like this, but this time for the purpose of awaiting the scrapper's torch. They were in good shape, but their final resting place became a boneyard, where they were cut up into pieces and hauled away. Decisions to scrap donkeys wholesale were cold-blooded and harsh, but in every way understandable. The largest and best equipment provided the most payload for the eager scrappers, irrespective of mechanical condition. *Oregon Historical Society, W.I.S.Co. Collection, OrHi 92949*

DEDICATION

**To the loggers who were there, especially
my father, R. Lee Johnson (1885-1981)**

Winter logging, high lead style. On this show, logs were yarded from across the creek to the landing, then loaded with a crotch line on the railroad. Typical of the times, houses on donkeys appear to be makeshift, battered contrivances. Appearances, however, were in no way indicative of the kind of operation or mechanical condition of the equipment one would expect to see. Note the boards between the house and water tank to aid in cutting out some of the winter elements. There is nothing like a toasty-warm donkey on a winter day! *Weister Co. photographers of Portland, Oregon, Meyer/Amel Collection, date and company unknown*

CONTENTS

Foreword   8

Introduction   9

  What is a Steam Donkey?   11

  Oregon Donkeys Extant   12

  Oregon Donkeys on Public Display   13

  Explanation of Dimensioning Style   15

  Anatomy of a Steam Donkey   15

  Chapter 1   **Vertical Spool Donkeys**   16

  Chapter 2   **Wide Face Donkeys**   24

  Chapter 3   **Compound Geared Yarders**   76

  Chapter 4   **Loaders**   128

  Chapter 5   **McGiffert Loaders**   160

  Chapter 6   **Incline Engines**   174

  Chapter 7   **Miscellaneous Related Steam Equipment**   192

  Chapter 8   **Models and Scale Drawings**   240

Appendix   264

  Author's Notes   266

  Organizations in Oregon with Significant Material on Logging   267

  Glossary   268

  Whistle Signals   270

  Additional Rigging Diagrams   271

  Some Suggestions for Continued Steam Donkey Research and News   274

Bibliography   275

Acknowledgments   276

Index   278

FOREWORD

For centuries the logger relied on animal power to move his logs. But the Industrial Revolution and the harnessing of the power of steam came as the answer to a logger's prayers. Skid roads had already reached the limits that the plodding bulls could handle efficiently, but the forests extended far beyond these limits. In the beginning it was the steam motive power that caught the logger's attention. Long before the Civil War, progressive loggers were extending their tram roads deep into the newly available timber. The locomotives were crude, and the roads often laid with wooden rails or poles, but the economic advantages were tremendous. It would be the 1880s before the power of steam was adapted to yarding and loading, but once begun, the new technology quickly became the norm. The speed, the power, and the efficiency of steam soon made all other logging methods obsolete. The use of steam expanded day by day until it reached its zenith in the 1920s. These were the "Glory Days" of logging.

John T. Labbe

An early Humboldt yarder owned by the Peninsula Lumber Company of Columbia City, Oregon, just a few miles north of St. Helens, Oregon. Willamette Iron & Steel started building Humboldts around 1906. Production continued well into the 1920s, outselling all other types of donkeys made by Willamette with many hundreds built. With their compound gearing and tremendous pulling ability, they proved very popular, and were used extensively for ground lead yarding. When high-lead yarding came into its own, these machines were quickly adapted to the job. *John T. Labbe Collection*

WHY STEAM DONKEYS?

Steam logging equipment has marked our journey through time as the West Coast became a part of national industrialization. Steam donkeys, in particular, were machines whose use typified the heyday of logging in the West, machines whose power and grace left a mark on the men as well as the mountains. Those steam donkeys that still exist create a three dimensional scrapbook of history. Donkeys are, as one writer put it, a link to the "glory days of logging." Those who worked the "big woods" around the steamers speak of that time, now gone forever, with reverent nostalgia. However, it is not necessary to be a steam logging equipment lover to mourn the demise of steam donkeys in Oregon. While you don't have to like donkeys or logging history, it is important to realize that (1) of the thousands that were built during the age of steam, and used in Oregon, only about forty remain in Oregon; (2) of these, only a few are anywhere near operating condition; and (3) almost all donkeys built prior to 1930 were steam powered. How could these machines have disappeared so fast? Why have the traces been almost totally erased? Were the Willamette two-speeds, the Lidgerwood skidders, and the duplex loaders only devices used to transport logs from stump to railroad, useful then, but now forgotten?

These steamers were central to the character of mechanized logging of the time. Each machine had its own personality, its own idiosyncrasies, unlike today (today, the engineer climbs into an enclosed cab and pushes an electric starter). The donkey was unique in so many ways, even in its sounds. How many know what a donkey sounds like? Even among steam railroad fans, few are familiar with the powerful sound of hot, dry steam powering a 12x14 yarder pulling at high speed. It is unlike anything else. The power, the speed, the vibration, the smell were all part of it. For some today, the odor of crude oil, freshly cut wood, or a frying sound of lubrication, will trigger an instant time machine. The memories of those days we prefer to recall are of a time of glamour, accomplishment, humor, and hard work, in spite of facing danger, pain and sometimes death.

To understand how deeply the steam donkeys cut into the logger's personal history, it is only necessary to talk to those who were there. But one must hurry, for time is taking its toll. Their numbers are diminishing. Some died before they could be contacted about the history of donkeys remaining in Oregon.

Many of the stories still remain, however. I remember my father, Lee Johnson, warming toast over the firebox extension. I remember Lee steam-cleaning his overalls with his homemade washing machine connected to a donkey. I also remember, during World War II, riding in a '41 Chevy pickup between the shoulders of two loggers[*] who were reminiscing about Consolidated Timber Company, which had shut down its steam a year previously. Both of them had spent most of their lives on and around donkeys. Their vivid descriptions of how yarders sounded with 225 pounds of steam in a hard pull, how the firebox door would puff after a turn of logs came in, and how one could tell a "whistle punk" by his style of blowing whistles brought tears to my eyes that day.

Let's zero in on a part of us, the part that doesn't want to sever these roots. One way to prevent that separation of ourselves from our past is to revive the romance of steam logging.

Merv Johnson

[*] Lee Johnson and Ted Anderson

In this factory photograph, a dozen steam donkeys take form in one of Willamette Iron & Steel Works' erecting bays, in Portland, Oregon. *Steven R. Gatke Collection*

In Search of Steam Donkeys

WHAT IS A STEAM DONKEY?

What is a steam donkey? Walter McCulloch, in his book, *Woods Words*[*], has a lot to say about the term "donkey." The following is from his dictionary:

> **Donkey** - a. An endless variety of steam, gas, diesel, or electric power plants, plus drums to hold wire rope; all used to haul logs from the woods, to load at landings, move equipment, rig up trees, and in the old days, to lower cars down inclines. . . . The most common makes were Seattle, Portland, Tacoma, named after iron works in those cities, Vulcan, Smith and Watson, and others named after the company which built them. . . . 26 different types of steam donkeys were built in the Pacific Northwest by one firm alone. In 1913, one company built 51 donkeys in a 49 day period, all sold before they left the plant to fill rush orders...Donkey was a term originally applied to a little steam engine of less than one horsepower. Dolbeer adapted a ship's capstan for his logging rig, and it is possible that he also brought along the seafaring term for the engine itself.

In later years, however, some donkeys manufactured were of enormous size. For example, one "unit skidder" was so large it had to be mounted on two railroad cars.[§]

Steam was generated by heat from wood, coal or oil fuel in the firebox and was supplied to the reciprocating engines. With a few exceptions, steam donkeys had vertical boilers. The later models were well-designed machines that were more than adequate for the job. Some were rather complicated machines with compressed air to operate controls. They were not built to the close tolerances of the machines of today, which, in turn, often permitted on-the-spot repairs by the loggers.

As with locomotives, the downfall of steam equipment occurred because of competition with efficiency and labor costs as the diesel engine was perfected. The late model steam donkeys had plenty of power and speed. A quarter turn of the throttle would provide full power with unbelievable low end torque and acceleration, but it took a lot of fuel to deliver the power. The engines were extremely dependable and long-lived, but the boilers required regular maintenance and water. The former was a factor in labor costs, and the latter, water, wasn't always readily available. Last, but not least, was the problem of fire danger created by these machines working in the woods.

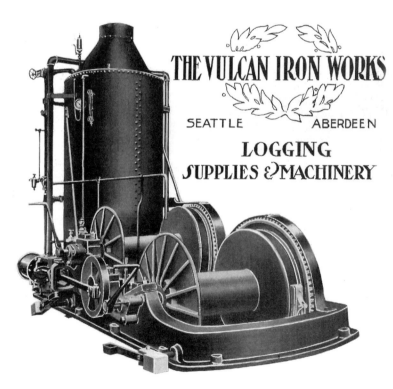

THE VULCAN IRON WORKS

SEATTLE   ABERDEEN

LOGGING SUPPLIES & MACHINERY

Advertisement from The Timberman, Jan., 1907.
Tim Anderson Collectiom

[*] Walter F. McCulloch, *Woods Words*, Oregon Historical Society and the Champoeg Press, 1958, p. 49.
[§] Willamette Iron & Steel Works, *Logging Machinery Catalogue*, Portland, Oregon, 1925, p. 39.

Oregon Donkeys Extant

List of Known Existing* Donkeys

NO.	BUILDER	TYPE	LOCATION	OWNER	B	S	P	Page
1	Marscutz & Cantrell	vertical spool	Elsie	Camp 18 Logging Museum	X	X	X	18
2	Moore & Scott	vertical spool	North Bend	Coos Historical Organization	X	X	X	20
3	Moore Ship Bldg.	vertical spool	Chiloquin	Collier Logging Museum	X	X	X	23
4	W.I.S.Co.	wide face	Creswell	Creswell High School	X		X	29
5	P.S.I.&S.W.	wide face yarder	Tillamook	Tillamook Co. Pioneer Museum	X	X	X	31
6	W.I.W.	wide face	Elsie	Camp 18 Logging Museum	X			41
8	P.S.I.&S.W.	wide face	Elsie	Camp 18 Logging Museum	X	X	X	43
9	Mundy	wide face	Elsie	Camp 18 Logging Museum	X		X	45
10	P.S.I.& S.W.	wide face	private display	David Parsons	X		X	47
11	P.S.I.&S.W.	wide face	Chiloquin	Collier Logging Museum	X	X	X	50
12	W.I.S.Co.	wide face	private display	Steve Beranek	X		X	52
13	W.I.W.	wide face	Garibaldi	Lumberman's Park	X	X	X	54
14	unknown	wide face	private display	Glen Stevens	X	X	X	57
15	Lidgerwood	wide face	Tillamook	Homer Simmons	X		X	60
16	W.I.W	wide face	private display	Mr. Walker	X	X	X	62
17	W.I.S.Co.	wide face (roader)	Powers	Coos County	X		X	68
18	W.I.S.Co.	wide face (roader)	private display	Lulay Bros.	X	X	X	69
19	W. I. W.	wide face	Vernonia	Columbia County Hist. Museum	X	X	X	71
20	A.H.&D.	wide face	private	Danny Hongell	X			71
21	W.I.W.	wide face	private display	Overholzer	X	X	X	72
22	O.&S.	wide face	Blue River	Dave Knapp	X	X	X	73
23	A.H.&D.	wide face (hoist)	Milwaukie	Al Foglio	X	X	X	74
24	A.H.&D.	wide face	private display	Loren Wilton			X	74
25	Clyde	wide face (hoist)	Elsie	Camp 18 Logging Museum	X	X	X	75
26	Clyde	wide face (hoist)	Elsie	Camp 18 Logging Museum	X	X	X	75
27	W.I.S.Co.	Humboldt yarder	private display	Jack Himebaugh	X		X	81
28	W.I.S.Co.	Humboldt yarder	Tillamook Forest	State Forest Service	X		X	84
30	W.I.W.	C.G. yarder	Tillamook Forest	State Forest Service	X	X	X	90
31	S.&W.	C.G. 2sp yarder	Roseburg	Douglas County Museum	X	X	X	92
32	S.&W.	C.G. yarder	Dallas	Willamette Industries			X	98
33	W.I.S.Co.	Humboldt yarder	Coast Range	Boise Cascade Corp.	X	X	X	100
34	P.S.I.&S.W.	C.G. yarder	Coast Range	Sparrow-Crow	X	X	X	104
35	W.I.S.Co.	C.G. 2sp yarder	Elsie	Camp 18 Logging Museum	X	X	X	108
36	S.&W.	C.G. yarder	Reedsport	Reedsport Discovery Center	X	X	X	123
37	W.I.S.Co.	loader	Elsie	Camp 18 Logging Museum	X	X	X	134
38	W.I.S.Co.	loader	Elsie	Camp 18 Logging Museum	X		X	138
39	W.I.S.Co.	loader	private display	Giustina Bros.	X	X	X	143
40	Clyde	McGiffert loader	Chiloquin	Collier Logging Museum	X	X	X	164
41	Clyde	McGiffert loader	Chiloquin	Collier Logging Museum	X	X	X	166
43	Clyde	track layer	Chiloquin	Collier Logging Museum	X		X	202

LEGEND:
- No.   Machine No. (sequence in this book)
- B   boiler
- S   sled, etc.
- P   90% of parts remain

* Machines No. 7, 29 and 42 are not listed above as they have either been scrapped or moved out of the state

Oregon Donkeys on Public Display
as of January, 1996
(Item numbers correspond to machine numbers)

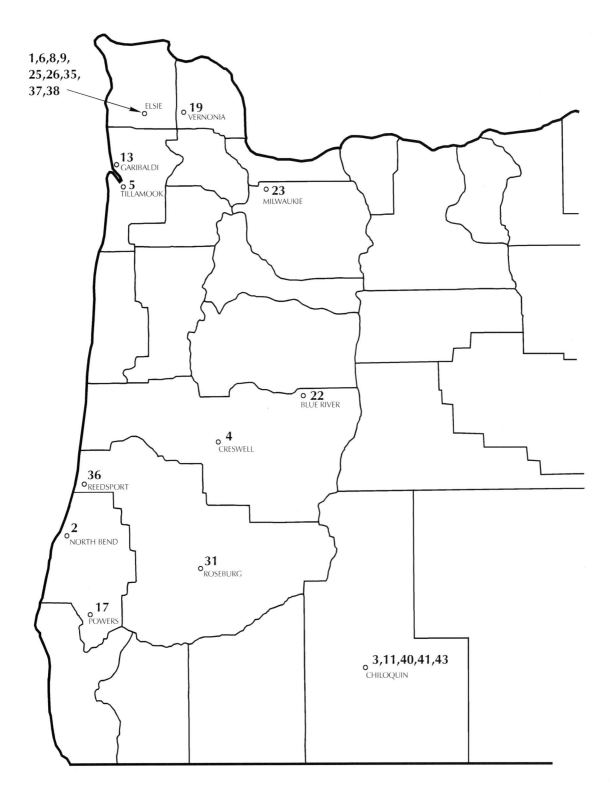

1,6,8,9,
25,26,35,
37,38

ELSIE

19
VERNONIA

13
GARIBALDI

5
TILLAMOOK

23
MILWAUKIE

22
BLUE RIVER

4
CRESWELL

36
REEDSPORT

2
NORTH BEND

31
ROSEBURG

17
POWERS

3,11,40,41,43
CHILOQUIN

Note: Machine No.s 12, 14, 16, 18, 20, 24, 27, and 39 are not included because they are not on public display.

Above   Moving a donkey across a bridge under its own power. Note the crude bridge construction—this may have been built as a temporary structure to get the donkey across the ravine.
Unidentified from W.I.S.Co.
Oregon Historical Society
OrHi No. 92945

Left   Moving a donkey was sometimes a difficult and hazardous operation. Caution and foresight were needed to keep from getting stuck and to prevent runaways.
Unidentified from W.I.S.Co.
Oregon Historical Society
OrHi No. 92943

EXPLANATION OF DIMENSIONING STYLE

All dimensions are approximate.

All dimensions are in inches unless stated otherwise.

If fireboxes are extended, dimensions are given, otherwise same as boiler.

H. B. - haulback (trip) drum.

Frame sizes are outside dimensions.

Frames are usually "I" beam (see illustration at right).

P. D. - gear pitch diameter at point of intersection.

Boiler heights do not include the smokebox.

Smokebox height is from top of boiler to the smoke stack (see illustration at right).

Sometimes brakes have different diameters than drum flanges (see illustration at right).

Diameters are listed first, e.g.:
> Cylinder bore and stroke = 12" dia. x 14" stroke.
> Drum core D/W = 9" dia. x 35" wide.

Crank disk width is the thickness of the disk.

Drum core diameter is unknown if there is cable on the drum.

Additional dimensions are available in some cases.

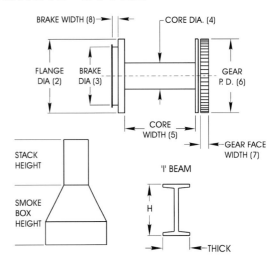

	FLANGE DIA	CORE D/W	GEAR & BRAKE	
			PD	F/ WIDTH
DRUM	2	4/5	6	7
BRAKE	3			8

THE ANATOMY OF A STEAM DONKEY

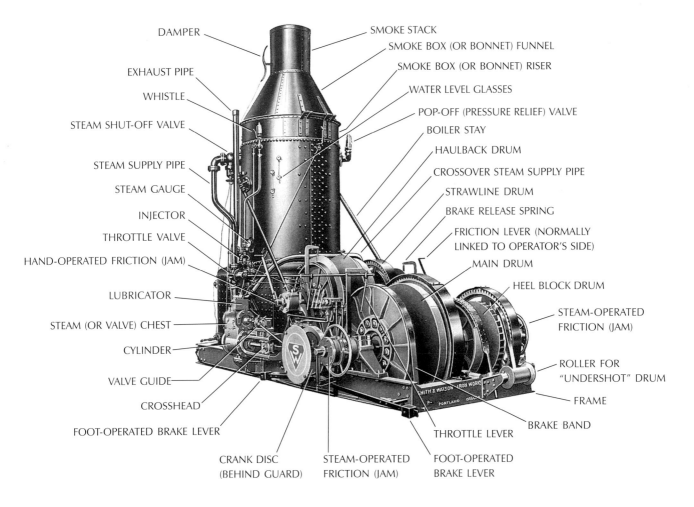

DAMPER

EXHAUST PIPE

WHISTLE

STEAM SHUT-OFF VALVE

STEAM SUPPLY PIPE

STEAM GAUGE

INJECTOR

THROTTLE VALVE

HAND-OPERATED FRICTION (JAM)

LUBRICATOR

STEAM (OR VALVE) CHEST

CYLINDER

VALVE GUIDE

CROSSHEAD

FOOT-OPERATED BRAKE LEVER

CRANK DISC (BEHIND GUARD)

STEAM-OPERATED FRICTION (JAM)

FOOT-OPERATED BRAKE LEVER

SMOKE STACK

SMOKE BOX (OR BONNET) FUNNEL

SMOKE BOX (OR BONNET) RISER

WATER LEVEL GLASSES

POP-OFF (PRESSURE RELIEF) VALVE

BOILER STAY

HAULBACK DRUM

CROSSOVER STEAM SUPPLY PIPE

STRAWLINE DRUM

BRAKE RELEASE SPRING

FRICTION LEVER (NORMALLY LINKED TO OPERATOR'S SIDE)

MAIN DRUM

HEEL BLOCK DRUM

STEAM-OPERATED FRICTION (JAM)

ROLLER FOR "UNDERSHOT" DRUM

FRAME

BRAKE BAND

THROTTLE LEVER

The logging operation of J.C. Trullinger, on the Walluski River, 1889. Trullinger operated out of Astoria, Oregon and was the first railroad operation on the Oregon side of the Columbia River. This vertical spool (Dolbeer) donkey is being used to parbuckle logs onto the cars. Note the tiny Porter engine.   *John T. Labbe Collection*

CHAPTER 1
VERTICAL SPOOL DONKEYS

The vertical spool or "Dolbeer" donkey (named for its inventor) marked the beginning of mechanized methods of moving timber about. Although small enough to be considered a "toy" by later standards, the Dolbeer was able to move logs lying in "... inconvenient and inaccessible places..." which "...run from four feet to twelve feet in diameter..."* In California it was not unusual to handle logs as large as fifteen feet in diameter, using a six or eight-block purchase.

---

* United States patent office, John Dolbeer Logging Engine, Patent 256,553 (this patent preceded the vertical spool donkey by one year, making the above patent date 1883, #290,755. His drawings are reproduced on pages 21 and 23.

Machine No. 1 at Camp 18 Logging Museum near Elsie, Oregon.   *Merv Johnson photo, 1983*

This is one of the few existing Oregon donkeys that is in operating condition. Gordon Smith enlisted the aid of Stanley Mathews to restore it to operating condition. They had it under steam in time for the Clark & Wilson Lumber Co. reunion picnic at Camp 18 Logging Museum in 1981, where it is shown in the photo.

Previous to its present location, this Dolbeer, and a Willamette loader (now also at this museum) were housed at a machine shop in Milwaukie, Oregon. They were moved there from Delta Park in Portland. Previous to Delta Park, they were on display near the old Forestry Building on Vaughn Street in Portland until the building burned. This donkey and the Willamette were donated during or after 1956 under the auspices of the "Forest Park Committee of Fifty," which was attempting to acquire vintage logging equipment.

Additional data:
   Boiler 36 diameter x 84 high,
   Boiler #6329-18
   Smoke stack diameter 12,
   Steam supply pipe 1-1°
   Firebox door 9-°x16
   No frame

OWNER	Camp 18 Logging Museum				Machine #1
Location	Elsie, Oregon				
Builder	Marschutz & Cantrell				
Type	Vertical Spool Dolbeer				
Bore & Stroke	6 X 12				
	D	W	L		H
PINION GEAR	5-1/2				
FLY-WHEEL	34	5			
BULL GEAR	5				
	FLANGES	CORE	GEAR PD		
GYPSY	16	11	50 (tapered)		

B oth Dolbeer photos on this page are from the Transportation and Logging Museum of Portland, Oregon, which once had custody of Oregon Machine No. 1 (and also Machine No. 37 which is shown on page 135 of this book). In 1977 this Portland-based organization hoped to house the orphaned donkeys that were near the old Forestry Building on Vaughn Street before it burned. The photo to the right, from the same file, was taken in 1956 when the search was on for a suitable donkey for the Vaughn Street location. It is believed of the upper photo that the location is Klamath Falls, Oregon, in the 1880s at Lou Parson's Camp 3.

MACHINE NO. 2

This vertical spool donkey in North Bend, Oregon was manufactured in San Francisco at the National Iron Works by Marschutz and Cantrell in 1902 under a Dolbeer patent*, according to the Coos County Pioneer and Historical Association. It was shipped to Coos County to the Simpson Logging Co. and was first used on Blue Ridge, Oregon in Simpson's logging camp. Later it was used in operations on Daniels Creek on the Coos River. In 1904 Simpson sold it to Emmet Pierce who then took it to the upper north fork of the Coquille River. About 1905, Pierce sold it to Jack McDonald. McDonald took William Vaughn in as his partner and they formed the company of McDonald and Vaughn. The throttle of the donkey was redesigned and built by Mr. George Terry about 1908[§].This donkey was used to build roads, bridges, and everything else a donkey can be used for. About 1917 or 1918, the firm of McDonald and Vaughn became the Coos Bay Lumber Co. Vaughn had various other pieces of logging equipment which he sold, but he would never part with this donkey as he was sentimentally attached to it, because it was his first. It was used until July 1950. He presented it to the Coos County Pioneer and Historical Association on July 30, 1950. This may have been the last spool donkey to operate in Oregon.

An historical account according to Rolph Hongell, who was a longtime Coos County resident:

My father, Alex Hongell, worked for Simpson Logging Co. when this spool donkey was being used. The buckers were cutting near the donkey as it was in operation. An old growth tree once slid down the hill toward the donkey. Alex tried to attract the donkey crew's attention by yelling and throwing bark chips into the air. On its way toward the donkey, it took the saw out of a bucker's hand without hurting him, and continued on down toward the donkey. The log hit the donkey on the rear guard and continued further down the hill and came to a rest against a cedar tree. Later, Alex needed to buck the tree. As he was wedging it, a metal chip flew off, as they sometimes do, embedding itself in his leg. That was the only injury that day! That piece of steel was in his leg years later.

* Bill Hudson lists the manufacturer of this donkey as Moore and Scott.

§ According to Bill Hudson, modifications to the throttle were made in California in earlier years, as evidenced by various photos in books on Redwood logging by John Labbe or Hank Johnston.

OWNER Location Builder Type Bore & Stroke	Coos Historical Organization City Park, North Bend, Oregon Marschutz & Cantrell Vertical Spool Dolbeer 6 X 12				Machine #2
	D	W	L	SHAFT	H
PINION GEAR	6			3	
FLY-WHEEL	30	6			
BOILER	36				
	FLANGES	CORE	GEAR PD		
GYPSY	16-upper 18-lower 9-core	height 16	52 bevel		

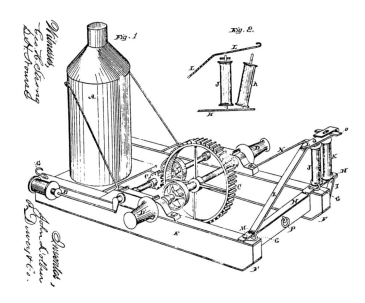

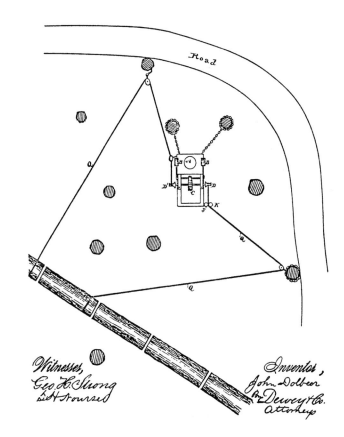

Above and right These are the original patent drawings filed by John Dolbeer in 1882. This was for the original design, which had a horizontal spool.

Below This unidentified view shows many elements of early steam logging, including ground lead yarding and a mule used to pack water in canvas bags. The horizontal-spool Dolbeer donkey matches the patent drawings above. *Steven Gatke Collection*

Above An unusual 2-cylinder vertical spool engine owned by Amund Ellingson Logging Company of Grays Harbor County, Washington. *Photo from Scott Elser Collection via John T. Labbe*

Below A horizontal-spool Dolbeer donkey at work in the woods near Mad River in the California Coastal redwood region. This was the John Vance Mill & Lumber Co. *A.W. Ericson photo from L. Carranco Collection via John T. Labbe*

Below This early photograph shows a horizontal-spool Dolbeer donkey yarding logs for Bridal Veil Lumber Co., east of Portland, Oregon on the Columbia River. The horse was used to return the line to the woods. *John T. Labbe Collection*

In Search of Steam Donkeys

| OWNER
Location
Builder
Type
Bore &
Stroke | Collier Logging Museum
Chiloquin, Oregon
Moore Ship Building Co.
Vertical Spool Dolbeer

6 X 12 | | Machine
#3 | |

	D	W	L	H
PINION GEAR	6 (tapered)	5		
FLY-WHEEL	30	6		
BRAKE BAND		2		

	FLANGES	CORE	GEAR PD	WIDTH
SPOOL	15/17	10/16	50	5

Additional data:
Spool Shaft 3" D.
Boiler 40" D.
Steam supply pipe 1.5" D
Exhaust pipe 2" D.
Firebox door 9" x 15"
Square wooden water tank

Vertical-spool donkeys had no "drum" (a later term). The vertical spool, or "gypsy" was used to pull in logs by having several wraps around it for friction, which meant a "spool tender" was needed to coil up the loose end of the cable on the ground as the log was pulled in. To return the rigging to the woods, animal or human power was needed.

These machines were equipped with a guard around the bull gear, but this shield got lost on some donkeys. The four shackles on the plate below the spool were used for securing to a tree or stump as an anchor against the pull of the log (see the Dolbeer patent drawings below and on page 21).

Above Machine No. 3 on display at the Collier State Logging Museum near Chiloquin, Oregon. *Photo by the author, 1977*

Below Boiler drawing, Machine No. 3, by the author

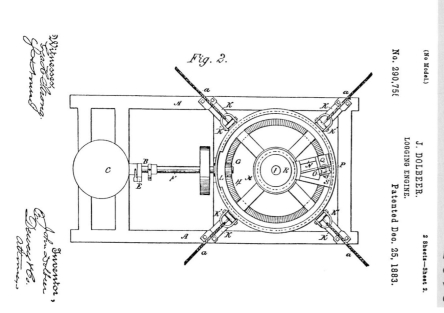

Fig. 2.

(No Model.)

No. 290,756.

J. DOLBEER.
LOGGING ENGINE.
Patented Dec. 25, 1883.

2 Sheets—Sheet 2.

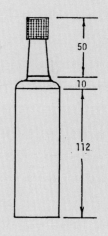

Left Dolbeer's patent drawing for his second design, which used a vertical spool. This patent was granted on December 25, 1883. *Courtesy Bill Hudson*

Vertical Spool Donkeys

CHAPTER 2
WIDE FACE DONKEYS

The term "wide face" refers to the drum width, i.e. those with drums wider in proportion than the later high lead machines.

These donkeys could have been used for a number of operations. For example, ground lead (dragging logs on the ground), or high lead (logs yarded with one or both ends in the air), or some may have been used for loading operations.

Opposite   This downed tree made a most unusual
if not practical roof for this early Mundy wide face road engine.
This engine is similar to Machine No. 9, shown on page 45.
Mundy donkeys, manufactured in Newark, New Jersey, were
popular with loggers at the turn of the century. The photo
location is unidentified.   *Steven Gatke Collection*

Left   Arthur Smith was killed when this donkey blew up in 1908 at Bridal Veil Lumber Company. This donkey was located close to the Palmer Mill near Bridal Veil Creek. Although the exact cause of this accident has not been verified, explosions such as this were usually caused by a low water level, or poor boiler maintenance.
Photo courtesy of Lewis Faught

Below   Ground lead logging. Date and location unknown.   *Lee Johnson Collection*

Right A wide face road engine used to bring logs to the rollway for loading onto railroad cars. This is the operation of Smith-Powers Logging Co. of Marshfield, Oregon. The No. 1, a 28-ton Shay, was quite new when this photograph was taken in 1907. *Jack's Photo Service from John T. Labbe*

Below C.K. Spaulding Logging Co's. Ritter Creek operation. This is Dave Simpson's early Mundy donkey at the head of the log chute above Hoskins, Oregon. *Dee Simpson photo from Lloyd Palmer*

The new and the old. Creswell High School has been a leader in alternative energy education. At the time these photos were taken, (1981) students nearby were involved in solar energy activities. The preservation of the old, and the dawning of a new age? This machine was delivered in Sept. of '79 to Creswell High School. Due to the large, wide drums, this may have been sold as a road engine. It appears to have been equipped with a bleeder valve, which allows lowering on compression. Also, note the single extended firebox on the boiler. Willamette introduced this type of firebox in 1911. They came out with the double-extended firebox (shown on page 82) in 1920. *Photos by the author*

Above Machine No. 4, A Willamette Iron & Steell Works 11 x 13 "roader," on display at Creswell High School in Creswell, Oregon. *Author's photo*

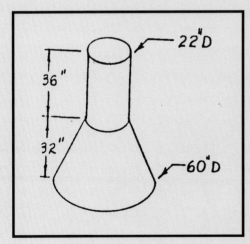

Drawing by author

Additional data:
Firebox opening - 16x22
Pinion shaft - 4-3/4 Dia.

OWNER	Creswell High School				Machine #4
Location	Creswell, Oregon				
Builder	Willamette Iron & Steel				
Type	Wide Face				
Bore & Stroke	11 X 13				
	D	W	L	THICK	H
FRAME SIZE		77-1/2	16'-6"	6	15
PINION GEAR	9.3	6			
CRANK DISC	30	3-3/4			
FIREBOX		60	86		58-1/2
BOILER	60				135
SMOKEBOX	60				32
	FLANGE DIA	CORE D/W	GEAR & BRAKE PD	F/ WIDTH	SHAFT DIA
MAIN DRUM	51	17/44-1/2	60	6	5-1/4
MAIN BRAKE	40-1/2			3	
H/B DRUM	40	20.5/43.5	38	6	4-1/2
H/B BRAKE	34			3	
STRAW DRUM	36	28/5-1/2			
STRAW BRAKE	27			2-1/4	

Above   A Washington Iron Works wide face roader working somewhere in Oregon's Cascades, about 1920. Note the sloping valve chest on the cylinder, a distinctive spotting feature of early Washington Iron Works donkeys.   *Martin E. Hansen Collection*

Left   McDonald and Vaughn's logging operation at Daniels Creek, a tributary of the Coos River in Coos County, Oregon. The logs are being roaded to the rollway by one donkey, and rolled onto the disconnected cars by the other donkey. The railroad was operated by Simpson Lumber Co. of Marshfield (now Coos Bay). The trim 4-4-0 came from the O.R.&N. This was near the turn of the century. *Philip Schnell Collection*

In Search of Steam Donkeys

Above Machine No. 5, a Tacoma wide face donkey, on display in Tillamook, Oregon. *Author's photo*

Left and lower left Occasionally, the old "Tacoma" gets fired up for the enjoyment of the locals. Rigged with two whistles, her nostalgic sounds can be heard all over town. Arlo Moffert is the engineer in the photos. *Philip Schnell photos, 1995*

OWNER Location Builder Type Bore & Stroke	Tillamook Pioneer Museum Tillamook, Oregon Puget Sound Iron & Steel Works "Tacoma" Wide Face Yarder 9 X 10				Machine #5
	D	W	L	THICK	H
FRAME SIZE		67	144	5	14
PINION GEAR	7	4-1/4			
CRANK DISC	20	3			
BOILER	52				114
	FLANGE DIA	CORE D/W	GEAR & BRAKE PD	F/ WIDTH	SHAFT DIA
MAIN DRUM	37	/38	48	4-1/2	3-3/4
MAIN BRAKE	28			2-1/2	
H/B DRUM	32	/38	30	4-1/2	3-3/4
H/B BRAKE	28			2-1/2	
STRAW DRUM	27	/8	(main drum)	4-1/2	3-3/4
STRAW BRAKE				2-1/2	

MACHINE NO. 5

BACKYARD LOGGING, FAMILY STYLE

The logging industry probably has more than its share of stories. Some are humorous. Ned Rieger's brother Joe used to run Machine No. 5. Like many, it had a seat attached to the running board. This seat at one time leaned out over a sea of mud. One day, there was an

unexpected pause in operations. The cause was found to be one yarder engineer, seat first in the mud, attempting to extricate himself!

Rieger family photographs showing Machine No. 5 in action, taken prior to 1952. Courtesy of Tillamook Pioneer Museum

When the Riegers finished logging their place about 1952, Machine No. 5 and spar tree were abandoned and left intact. I have made several pilgrimages to that spot, up a road in which trees arched over my head, their growth reflecting the intervals between each trip. Eventually, wood rotted under the tree plates, causing the top of the spar tree to fall down, leaving guy lines and rigging in a pile. I remember a set of tongs, split wood still stacked behind the firebox, and water draining from the cylinder cocks when I pulled the lever. A rare find in the world of donkey searches! Seldom, if ever, does one find a donkey as complete as this that has been out in the woods for so long.   *Author's photo, 1975*

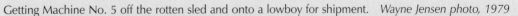

Getting Machine No. 5 off the rotten sled and onto a lowboy for shipment.   *Wayne Jensen photo, 1979*

THE RESTORATION OF A RELIC

The above photo is of the restoration effort of machine No. 5, spearheaded by Homer Simmons, retired logger. The Simmons brothers are building the sled in the spring of 1981. Wes, on the left, Granville in the center, and Homer on the right. A sad thing happened about 15 minutes after this photo was taken. Granville died suddenly of a massive heart attack. However, his part in preserving a segment of the logging era was appreciated. I asked him to remove his tin hat so my camera would depict the steam era as it was. He did, and now his last contribution as a sled builder is preserved on film in a rare occurrence in today's world.

Ned Rieger was the last one to log with this donkey. The location was on Rieger property near Tillamook which today is owned Ned's survivors. History previous to Ned Rieger on this donkey is vague, but Homer Simmons has, through interviews, determined that it could have been the one used near Netarts on what is now Crown Zellerbach land. This may have been the same donkey Wibb Ward and Johnny Thomas used to log at Sand Lake near a cheese factory. It eventually ended up at Steinback Iron Works at which time they were asking from $600 to $700 for it. If this was the case, Ned would have been the next owner, using it on his place, and shutting it down in 1952. It was retrieved in 1979, and moved to the Tillamook Air Base for restoration as shown here. Machine 5 has subsequently been moved to and placed on display at the Tillamook County Pioneer Museum in Tillamook, Oregon.   *Merv Johnson photo*

CARE FOR AN
AFTERNOON OF FUN?
...NEXT PAGE

STEAM UP A DONKEY!

These photographs and the one on the previous page are by Jody Kollinzas taken in June, 1984 of Machine No. 5 at the Tillamook County Pioneer Museum. Shown are Wes Simmons, Sam Ward, Valerie Kollinzas and the author.

"Tacoma" Standard Road Engine
9x10

Figure 955.

Round or Extended Firebox Boiler. "D" Slide Valves. Eccentric or Outside Valve Gear. Automatic Positive Feed Oil Pump.

SPECIFICATIONS

Frame	Boiler	Gears	Drums	Shafts
15″ 60-lb. I Beams	48″ dia., 103″ high 163 2″ tubes 63½″ long. 175 lbs., W. P.	ALL STEEL	Main Drum 13″ bbl., 38½″ long. 37½″ flanges. 4,000 ft. $\frac{7}{8}$″ 3,000 ft. 1″ 2,250 ft. 1⅛″	Main 4″ dia.
With 48″ boiler 7½ x 10 ft. over all.		Main Gear 39″ dia., 4½″ face.		Trip 4″ dia.
	or	Trip Gear 30½″ dia., 4″ face.		Crank 3¾″ dia.
With 54″ boiler 7¾ x 12 ft. over all.	54″ dia., 125″ high 211 2″ tubes, 78″ long. 175 lbs., W. P.		Trip Drum 13″ bbl., 38½″ long. 32½″ flanges. 8,600 ft. ½″ 6,800 ft. 9/16″ 5,350 ft. ⅝″	

A factory illustration similar to Machine No. 5 from F.B. Mallory Machinery Catalog No. 6, Portland, Oregon.
Glen Comstock Collection

Left This large Tacoma roader is shown working near Buxton, Oregon in 1915. Donkeys built by Puget Sound Iron & Steel Works were often called "Tacomas." As this photograph shows, the company was an early advocate of piston valves. Note that the strawline (loading) drum is partially dismantled, missing its friction device and lever. *Dennis Leischner Collection from Robert Wenzel*

Below Buehner Lumber Company ran a large logging operation from two camps, one at Allegany, Oregon, and the other at Lakeside, on Tenmile Lake. Their sawmill was at North Bend. Here a large Willamette roader is yarding logs down to the bank of Eel Lake, a few miles northwest of Tenmile Lake. *C. Kinsey photograph from Martin E. Hansen Collection*

In Search of Steam Donkeys

Right This early road engine uses a roller mounted on the sled to lift the haulback line above the main drum. Note the rustic water tank and cable coiled on the ground. This scene is near Rainier, Oregon.
Steven Gatke Collection

Below The rollway of Erickson & Son of Quincy, a few miles northeast of Clatskanie, along the Columbia River in Northwest Oregon. The engine spotting cars is their No. 1, a 35-ton Climax, bought new in 1906.
Steven Gatke Collection

Wide Face Donkeys

Above   A photograph from the head end of a working donkey engine. Granville (Granny) Simmons leaning on the fairlead. Note the spark arrestor, spring pole and whistle in the background. Granny died while building a donkey sled in 1981 (see story on page 34). This photograph was taken near Simmons Creek in Tillamook County when the Simmons family logged with steam.   *Lorene Simmons Collection*

Below   Orchard Land & Timber Company used this Washington Iron Works 9-1/4 x 13 wide face yarder to drag logs to the pond at their mill at Divide, Oregon. Note the steam hose running off to the left, most likely used to power a steam dragsaw to cut logs to length before entering the mill. Also, there is a small v-flume supplying water to feed the boiler.   *Steven Gatke Collection*

This small hoist engine was converted to gasoline-power with a Cadillac engine and automatic transmission before steam engines were considered of historic interest. Gordon Smith used it rigged to a crotch-line as long as it would hold together. Later, Gordon removed the engine and transmission, acquired a boiler used for heating a shop near the Gales Creek Tavern and placed it on this frame in his museum near Elsie, Oregon. Although a quasi-restoration, this machine is nevertheless listed as a donkey extant in Oregon.

This hoist engine appears to be a Washington Iron Works machine because of the tapered flanges on the drums. It has a cast frame.

Below Moving day for this large donkey owned by Palmer & Owen, in 1914 near Kerry, Oregon. *John T. Labbe Collection*

Above Machine No. 6 on display at Camp 18 Logging Museum near Elsie, Oregon. *Author's photo*

OWNER Location Builder Type Bore & Stroke	Camp 18 Logging Museum Elsie, Oregon Washington Iron Works Wide Face cylinders removed				Machine #6
	D	W	L	THICK	H
FRAME SIZE		67	113	6-1/2	12
PINION GEAR	6	5			
CRANK DISC	removed				
FIREBOX					
BOILER	42				96
SMOKEBOX	34				36

	FLANGE DIA	CORE D/W	GEAR & BRAKE PD F/ WIDTH		SHAFT DIA
MAIN DRUM	42	15/32	41	5	4
MAIN BRAKE	40				
H/B DRUM	36	11/32	35	5	3-1/4
H/B BRAKE	34				

Machine No. 7 is a Smith & Watson Iron Works 9-1/4 x 10 wide face yarder with a Willamette boiler with extended firebox added later. This donkey was on private display in Ruch, Oregon. It has been moved to Washington State. *Author's photo*

This donkey was a difficult and rare find. Rare indeed is a donkey that is mostly complete in spite of years sitting out in the woods. Climatic conditions in Southern Oregon, plus a remote location on private property, were major contributors. Getting this shot in 1976 was not easy. Ruch, Oregon on a hot mid-afternoon was not what one would call a steam nut's paradise in the face of people and dogs who eyed us suspiciously.

In time, however, we managed to gain the property owner's confidence. We left that day with fond memories of an intriguing old miner, lots of steam equipment, and people who helped us in our quest. At the same time, we were relieved that we were not shot at (one person carried a rifle) when going through fences, "no trespassing" signs, and trying to get people to come out of their seemingly vacant dwellings.

Unfortunately, the owner of the steam donkey, "Shorty" Gustiss, has since died with his dreams of restoring it to operation. He wanted to re-flue the boiler at Willamette Iron & Steel Works in Portland. (I did not have the heart to tell him they discontinued the steam equipment line many years ago.) He planned to use the yarder to work his mine, but time was running out for Shorty. Perhaps his dreams contributed to his long life. Surely this elderly hermit must have considered the possibility of striking it rich.

There is a happy ending to this story. This donkey has since been moved to Washington State, and is in the possession of Bill Parson of Olympia, who restores steam donkeys.

Above and below Machine No. 8 under steam at Smith Tug & Barge in Rainier, Oregon sometime in the 1970s. *Author's photos*

W ould you believe two donkeys in operation in 1981? Would you believe both are wood fired and have their own boilers? Yes, all true. They were used to pull ships up to dry dock as needed at Smith Tug and Barge in Rainier, Oregon. When it came time to pull a ship up, they were fired by hand.

This machine and Machine No. 9 are "bleeder" valve equipped, which allows lowering the ships down to the water by compression. Bleeders were also used by the loggers when high-lead systems became more sophisticated. Lee Johnson installed one on a yarder he used. It appears that others thought of the same idea because Willamette offered them as optional equipment not long afterward. Bleeders were especially useful for handling equipment when rigging trees.

The original boiler on this machine was replaced in the late 1940s. This donkey came from Wisconsin Logging Company and was used between Oak Point and Stella, Washington before going to Smith Tug and Barge at Rainier, Oregon. Knappton Tow Boat Company bought out Smith in 1979, after which the donkeys were mothballed for a time. Ownership was transferred to the Pacific Maritime Museum at Astoria, Oregon, then to Jim Smith and Mike Leigh of Astoria, and by 1983 both were on location at their present site at the Camp 18 Logging Museum at Elsie, Oregon.

OWNER Location Builder Type Bore & Stroke	Camp 18 Logging Museum Elsie, Oregon Puget Sound Iron & Steel Works (Tacoma) Wide Face (S/N 1058) 10 x 11				Machine #8

	D	W	L	THICK	H
FRAME SIZE		78	177	6	15
PINION GEAR	8	6-1/2			
CRANK DISC	22-1/2	3			
BOILER	60				120
SMOKEBOX	34				34

	FLANGE DIA	CORE D/W	GEAR & BRAKE PD	F/ WIDTH	SHAFT DIA
MAIN DRUM	48	17/45	54	6	5
MAIN BRAKE	38				
H/B DRUM	42	33/44-1/2	38	5	4
H/B BRAKE	30			3-1/2	

MACHINE NO. 8

Above Machine No. 8 on its new sled being readied for display at Camp 18 Logging Museum near Elsie, Oregon. The engine has since received a house. *Author's photo*

Additional data:
Water tank labeled for "Prouty Lumber Co."
and is 54" in diameter x 72" long.

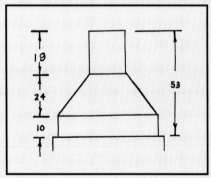

Smokebox drawing of Machine No. 5 by the author.

Right The Gales Creek Logging Co. moving crew had some explaining to do after this little mishap. This was at Glenwood, Oregon. It's not often that we get a worm's-eye view of a donkey sled. *Steven Gatke Collection*

Right Author's photo of Machine No. 9 on display at Camp 18 Logging Museum near Elsie, Oregon.

This little donkey was manufactured by the J.S. Mundy & Co. of Newark, New Jersey. It was used as a hoist on a ship after which Ericison & Klepp Shipyard in West Rainier, Oregon acquired it. The next owner was Jones Boatworks, who in turn sold it to Smith Tug & Barge in Rainier. This engine was used in the same shop as Machine No. 8 as a dry dock hoist engine by Smith Tug & Barge. Still in operation in 1981, both engine No. 8 and No. 9 were acquired by virtue of transfer of ownership to Knappton Tow Boat Co., then to the Pacific Maritime Museum at Astoria, until Smith and Leigh of Astoria attained them. Both donkeys were moved to the Camp 18 Logging Museum near Elsie, Oregon in early 1983.

Most of the Mundy hoists now in existence are small, but there is on record a 12 x 20 logging hoist built by Mundy. This engine was sold by Tatum and Bowen of San Francisco and Portland.

Right An ad that appeared in *The Timberman* in 1895. This ad was reproduced in the magazine's fiftieth anniversary issue. This engine is similar to Machine No. 9. *Philip Schnell Collection*

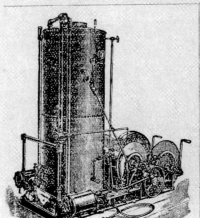

The Mundy Logging Engine·····

Built on Plans Furnished by Oregon and Washington Loggers.

Expert Testimony.

OAK POINT, WASH., Aug 24, 1895.

Messrs. TATUM & BOWEN,—Gentlemen:
We have one of your Mundy Logging Engines, which has been in use three years. It is a 12x20 cylinder. We haul our logs on a skid road the distance of a mile. A great part of the road is 9 feet grade to the 100 feet. Total grade to the mile 200 feet. Her actual running time for the round trip is thirty minutes, and we have hauled ten loads a day, and can haul 16,900 feet to a load, carrying only 60 pounds of steam. The cast steel gearing has not worn any. We have no trouble whatever with it. Having examined all other makes of Logging Engines, we consider our engine, as to workmanship, stability and material, to excel any we have ever seen. Our engine is as good today as the first day we run it.

Respectfully,
(Signed) J. B. WEIST & BROS.

Tatum & Bowen, Sole Agents,

85 Front Street, PORTLAND, 34-36 Fremont Street, SAN FRANCISCO.
Mundy's Engines and R. Hoe & Co's. Chisel Tooth Saws. . . . .

Above These photos were taken by the author when this donkey (No. 9) was used for pulling ships up to the dry dock at Rainier, Oregon in the 70s.

Below This unidentified photo is titled "moving day." It appears to be a Willamette Iron & Steel Works donkey. *Steven Gatke Collection*

Above Bleeder valve detail of Machine No. 9.

Additional data:
Pinion shaft—3-1/2"
W.I.S.Co. boiler, s/n 0-1362-51N

OWNER	Camp 18 Logging Museum				Machine
Location	Elsie, Oregon				#9
Builder	Mundy				
Type	Wide Face				
Bore & Stroke	7 x 10				

	D	W	L	THICK	H
FRAME SIZE		66	120	4-1/2	10-1/2
PINION GEAR	7				
CRANK DISC	23	3-1/2			
BOILER	45				96

	FLANGE DIA	CORE D/W	GEAR & BRAKE PD	F/ WIDTH	SHAFT DIA
MAIN DRUM	40	/29	43	5	4
MAIN BRAKE	35			3	
H/B DRUM	30	/29	30	5	3-1/2
H/B BRAKE	22			3	

These photos of Machine no. 10 were taken by the author at its current location. David Parsons is one of those rare people who has a steam donkey in his back yard!

OWNER	David Parsons				Machine
Location	Private display				#10
Builder	Puget Sound Iron & Steel Works (Tacoma)				
Type	Wide Face s/n 1149				
Bore & Stroke	10 x 12				

	D	W	L	THICK	H
FRAME SIZE		80	168	6-1/2	14-1/2
PINION GEAR	8				
CRANK DISC	22	3			
FIREBOX					
BOILER	60				144

	FLANGE DIA	CORE D/W	GEAR & BRAKE PD	F/ WIDTH	SHAFT DIA
MAIN DRUM	43	/38	55	6	4-1/2
MAIN BRAKE	36			3-1/2	
H/B DRUM	37	/38	37-1/2	5	4
H/B BRAKE	28			2	
STRAW DRUM	33	14.5/6.5			
STRAW BRAKE	24				

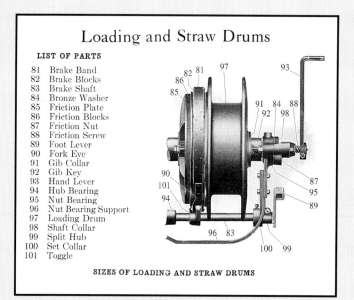

Loading and Straw Drums

LIST OF PARTS

81	Brake Band
82	Brake Blocks
83	Brake Shaft
84	Bronze Washer
85	Friction Plate
86	Friction Blocks
87	Friction Nut
88	Friction Screw
89	Foot Lever
90	Fork Eye
91	Gib Collar
92	Gib Key
93	Hand Lever
94	Hub Bearing
95	Nut Bearing
96	Nut Bearing Support
97	Loading Drum
98	Shaft Collar
99	Split Hub
100	Set Collar
101	Toggle

SIZES OF LOADING AND STRAW DRUMS

Above F.B. Mallory parts page showing outboard "loading" or "straw" drum arrangement for "Tacoma" engines. *Undated Mallory Catalogue No. 6, Glen Comstock Collection*

J.H. "Jack" Peterson Logging Co. at Rainier, Oregon circa 1900. This Mundy donkey is similar to Machine No. 9. Notice the semipermanent house covering the donkey, the vise, and the lamps overhead (just like home). This donkey was used to pull logs down from a log deck and push them down a chute. According to Lee Johnson, the men in the photograph from left to right are: Al Burns, Gus Nelson, unknown, and Robert Johnson.

This chute was near the house where Lee lived as a boy. Their house caught fire and Lee ran to tell his father (Robert, in the photograph). Unfortunately, Robert was doing maintenance at the bottom of the chute at the time. The chute was constructed on a steep pitch of ground nearing a cliff angle of descent to ensure that the logs would slide all the way to the bottom. Adrenaline shot into his system, and in desperation, Lee ran down the chute. Unfortunately, by the time he and his father returned to the top it was too late to save the house.

According to John Labbe, Jack Peterson challenged a Portland baseball team to a foot race some years later. This was at the Perkins Hotel at Fifth and Washington in Portland. According to John, this occurred about 1:30 in morning following a get-together in the bar. They agreed to remove their shoes and see who could get to the river first. At some point along the way, the team decided to head back to the bar, leaving Jack in the lead. Try to imagine a lone man, running full tilt without shoes in the middle of the night in downtown Portland. Unfortunately for Jack, the police took a dim view of the situation, and the next thing Jack knew he was in the police station trying to answer some embarrassing questions. *Lee Johnson Collection*

In Search of Steam Donkeys

Above In this unidentified view, a small donkey is being pulled onto a logging flatcar. The donkey doing the pulling is in the background. Note how the line has been doubled back several times in order to get enough pull to move the donkey. *Steven R. Gatke Collection*

Below An unidentified early rollway. Note the large wide face donkey for dragging the logs to the loading area and the small single-drum engine for gin-pole loading. *Philip Schnell Collection*

Wide Face Donkeys

Above Machine No. 11 as it appeared in 1976 at the Collier Logging Museum at Chiloquin, Oregon. It is unusual in that it has boiler lagging, and has a house built with pole construction. Not much information is available on this one. *Author's photo*

Below 10 x 12 "Tacoma" catalog cut, similar to Machine No. 11 *F.B. Mallory Catalogue No. 6, Glen Comstock Collection*

"Tacoma"
Standard
Road Engine

10x12

Figure 954
High Pressure Boiler. Balanced Slide Valves. Eccentric or Outside Valve Gear.
Automatic Positive Feed Oil Pump.
Furnished with Loading Drum, Steam or Special Friction and Extended Firebox Boiler
if Desired.

Additional data:
Pinion shaft - 4
Supply pipe - 2-1/2
Firebox door - 12 x 16
Boiler has lagging

OWNER	Collier Logging Museum				Machine #11
Location	Chiloquin				
Builder	Puget Sound Iron & Steel Works (Tacoma)				
Type	Wide Face s/n 1309				
Bore & Stroke	10 x 12				

	D	W	L	THICK	H
FRAME SIZE		78	171	6	15
PINION GEAR	6-1/2				
CRANK DISC	22	3			
BOILER	62				132

	FLANGE DIA	CORE D/W	GEAR & BRAKE PD	F/ WIDTH	SHAFT DIA
MAIN DRUM	42	22/39	54	6	5
MAIN BRAKE	35				
H/B DRUM	25	27/39	38	5-1/2	4
H/B BRAKE	25			2-3/8	
STRAW DRUM	32	20/7	(on main)		

Above   Technology comes to Forest Grove, Oregon. An early day arrival of steam power. This donkey is being moved by wagons (boiler in wagon behind) through Forest Grove, near Pacific University.

Below   Another unusual shot. Moving donkeys by their own power in downtown Newberg, Oregon.
Both Photographs from John T. Labbe Collection

MACHINE NO. 12

This small Willamette yarder was bought by its present owner, Steve Beranek, from an estate sale in Eugene, Oregon. It is believed to have been used at a mill in Sutherlin, Oregon. It now has a Washington Iron Works boiler. The boiler was originally used with a 9 x 10-1/4 loader (S/N 3880) delivered by Washington Iron Works in 1925.

OWNER	Steve Beranek				Machine
Location	Private Display				#12
Builder	Willamette Iron & Steel Works				
Type	Small Standard Yarder				
Bore & Stroke	8-1/2 x 10				

	D	W	L	THICK	H
FRAME SIZE		58	120	5	12
PINION GEAR	7	4-1/2			
CRANK DISC	20	3			
BOILER	50				96

	FLANGE DIA	CORE D/W	GEAR & BRAKE PD	F/ WIDTH	SHAFT DIA
MAIN DRUM	36	11/30	38	4-1/2	4
MAIN BRAKE	30			2	
H/B DRUM	28	12/30	31	4-1/2	3-1/2
H/B BRAKE	24			2	

Additional data:
Steam supply pipe - 2"
Firebox door - 11 x 18
Exhaust Pipes - 2-1/4

Above Machine No. 12 at its present location near Eugene, Oregon. *Author's photo, 1979*

Below A donkey after a boiler explosion, location unidentified. *OHS W.I.S.Co. Collection, OrHi 92937*

In Search of Steam Donkeys

This is the sort of thing that steam donkey fans dream about! This photograph is of the R.E. Barr operation near the Coweeman River in Washington State. The donkeys were used to yard into the river. Splash dams were then used to control movement of the logs down river. The timber in this area later developed some unusual wood grain. John Labbe recalls bidding on some timber in that area that was found to have coarse grain on the outer diameter of the logs. This unusual grain structure developed after a unit of timber was logged in the middle of tall, fine-grain trees. The trees near the open area that was logged grew at a rapid rate after that. When the surrounding timber was finally logged years later, the trees had coarse grain on the outer edge, rather than the normal opposite growth arrangement.   *John Labbe collection*

MACHINE NO. 13

OWNER Location Builder Type Bore & Stroke	Lumberman's Memorial Park Garibaldi Washington Iron Works Wide Face 8-1/2 x 10				Machine #13
	D	**W**	**L**	**THICK**	**H**
FRAME SIZE		67	132	5	9
PINION GEAR	6-1/2	4-1/2			
CRANK DISC	20	2			
BOILER	49				96
	FLANGE DIA	**CORE D/W**	**GEAR & BRAKE** **PD**	**F/ WIDTH**	**SHAFT DIA**
MAIN DRUM	38	12/35	48	4-1/4	4
MAIN BRAKE	32			3	
H/B DRUM	32	/35	30-1/2	4-1/4	3-1/4
H/B BRAKE	29			3	

Above Machine No. 13 at current location at Lumberman's Memorial Park in Garibaldi, Oregon. *Author's photo circa 1970s*

This donkey came from a mill near Castle Rock, Washington and was delivered to the Garibaldi Lions Club's Lumberman's Memorial Park in August 1969. The club purchased the donkey with funds from Lowell and Margaret Edwards. Margaret is the daughter of the late George Watt, pioneer Tillamook County lumberman. "Pat" Patterson spearheaded the project, Lee Johnson acted as consultant on the move and helped move it. Equipment used to load and move it was donated by Dick Schmitz Logging Company, Bildix Logging Company and Oregon-Washington Plywood Company. Among other people who helped were Wayne Dental, Jim Hawk, Mr. Davis (father of Ronald Davis from whom the club bought the donkey), Harold Brimmer and Harold Withrow.

Machine No. 13 has an oversize main drum gear (main drum gears are sometimes referred to as "bull" gears). This information from Pat Patterson and the article "Old Steam Pot Added to Garibaldi Collection," which appeared in the *Headlight Herald*, Tillamook, Oregon, Aug 21, 1969, p. 19.

Left A wide face donkey and crew take a break for the photographer at Henry Colvin's operation out of Marshland, Oregon, near O.K. Creek. *John Labbe Collection*

Above   Donkey modelers should be prepared for their fully-equipped donkey models to dwarf their locomotives! This appears to be a donkey about to be moved off the flatcar by its own power, in preparation for a new setting. This is the Robert C. Kinney Logging Company of Seaside, Oregon. Kinney's own railroad connected to the famous "Kerry Line" (Columbia & Nehalem River RR).   *Gordon Kinney Collection, John Labbe*

Below   Donkey boiler tube sheet with tubes removed. The world as it looks from the inside of a boiler.   *Merv Johnson*

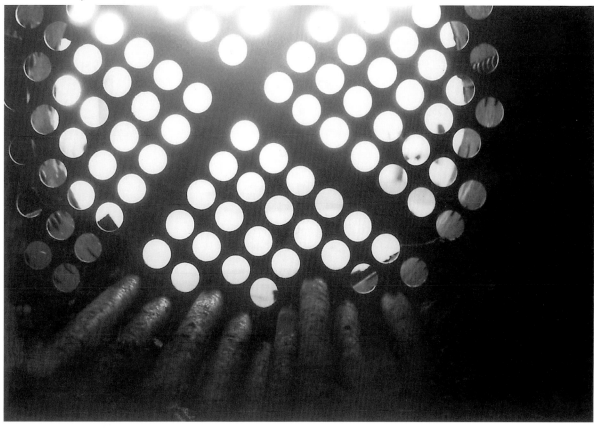

Donkey moving by the Meserve Brothers in the Grays Harbor, Washington area, circa 1910. Moving sled donkeys during most of the steam era involved a lot of labor because it was only possible to move a short distance on each tailhold. The crews were almost continually changing holds, which involved a lot of pulling straw line to position the new tail hold for the moving block. At the end of the day, arms felt as though they would fall off.

Donkeys with long sleds were easier to move than those with short sleds. Lee Johnson related a lengthy move of a large yarder and a smaller loader. The crew divided up between the two machines. As they prepared to leave, the last parting shots were a challenge as to who would arrive at the landing first. Unfortunately, the smaller loader was equipped with a short sled, which resulted in a much later arrival and a lot of extra work for the losers than faced by the winning crew with the yarder with the longer sled.   *Lee Johnson Collection*

In Search of Steam Donkeys

OWNER Location Builder Type Bore & Stroke	Glen Stevens Private Display unknown Wide Face 6 x 8			Machine #14	
	D	W	L	THICK	H
FRAME SIZE		51	90		
PINION GEAR	6	3			
CRANK DISC	15	2			
FIREBOX					
BOILER	36				72
	FLANGE DIA	CORE D/W	GEAR & BRAKE PD F/ WIDTH		SHAFT DIA
MAIN DRUM	23	10/26	24	3	2
H/B DRUM	24	13/26	26	3	2

Right   Author's photo of Machine
No. 14 at its present location

Thanks to Bill Ames and Glen Stevens, this little donkey was retrieved from the woods and is now on private property. According to Bill, this donkey was brought into the Hoskins, Oregon area before 1918. It was later transported on a six-horse wagon from Hoskins to Black Rock by George Gerlinger of Willamette Valley Lumber Co. There is a photograph of this machine in the book *Timber Up the Lukiamute* by W.C. "Pete" Frantz, pub. 1978. In the book it is shown with a different boiler and a sled that was shaped somewhat like a canoe. That was at Simpson Logging Co. at Hoskins, Oregon. The only manufacturer's identification on the entire machine is "O&S" stamped on the boiler. The original frame had only one drum; the front drum was an add-on. Both drums have right-hand friction screws.

Below   Booth-Kelly Lumber Company owned a large sawmill at Springfield, Oregon. They ran their logging operation from their camp at Wendling. This 1915 photograph shows two large Booth-Kelly donkeys at a setting above Wendling, Oregon.   *Steven Gatke Collection*

Wide Face Donkeys

This uphill move shows how adverse terrain was sometimes conquered. What a thrill it must have been to hear the last surge of power as it broke over the hump in the bottom photograph. *Unidentified, from L.P. Kremer Collection*

In Search of Steam Donkeys

GROUND LEAD LOGGING AT BENSON TIMBER COMPANY

Can you spot which one was Woods Boss for this Company? Albin Larson is remembered as a hard worker. He did whatever needed to be done, put in the hours needed to do it, lifted whatever needed to be lifted, and was not afraid to get his hands dirty. The fellow on the right was not a mechanic or donkey puncher, but the woods boss, Albin Larson. Unfortunately, his work ethic led to his early demise. He died at the age of 45 from causes related to this very difficult occupation. Photo location is either Camp Erickson or Camp Tichenor. *Photo and information courtesy of Rudolph Larson.*

OWNER	Homer Simmons			Machine
Location	Private Display			#15
Builder	Lidgerwood			
Type	Wide Face			
Bore & Stroke	9 x 10			

	D	W	L	THICK	H
FRAME SIZE		64	108	4	17-1/2
PINION GEAR	7	4			
CRANK DISC	22	2-1/4			
FIREBOX					
BOILER	45				108
SMOKEBOX					

	FLANGE DIA	CORE D/W	GEAR & BRAKE PD	F/ WIDTH	SHAFT DIA
MAIN DRUM	35	10/35	35	4	4
MAIN BRAKE	27			4	
H/B DRUM	31-1/2	9/35	30	4	3
H/B BRAKE	28			4	

From *The Timberman*, special 50th Anniversary issue, October, 1949. *Philip Schnell collection*

This type of Lidgerwood hoist was used before the turn of the century, according to an article in the October 1949 (50 year anniversary) issue of *The Timberman*. A reprint of an advertisement from the Cathlamet Gazette placed by J.M. Arthur, who was sales agent in Portland lists the following loggers on the Columbia River who were using their engines at that time: Benson and Co., L. Saldern, C.C. Masten, J.L. Masten, Lund and Carlson, Washougal Land and Logging Co., The Dalles Lumber Co., A.B. Root, Jr., Chitwood and Peterson, Marlow and Co., and J.B. Yeon.

Author's photo of Machine No. 15 at its present location, circa 1974

WASHINGTON WIDE FACE

This wood-burning donkey and crew are doing some winter logging in the snow for Benson Timber Company, Clatskanine, Oregon. The engineer, at the controls, is Mr. Lange (first name unknown). The man back by the cylinders was named "Columbia" Cross. The others are unidentified. *Clark Kinsey photograph, Rudolph Larson Collection.*

Machine No. 16 was last used as an incline engine to lower logs one car at a time to the mill. It was abandoned in 1941 at the spot where this photograph was taken. Claude and Alden Potter once owned this machine. They quit logging sometime after that in the late 40s. Judging by the looks of the main drum shaft, it may have had another drum, or gypsy at one time. *Author's photo, 1977*

OWNER	Mr. Walker				Machine
Location	Private Display				#16
Builder	Washington Iron Works				
Type	Wide Face				
Bore & Stroke	10 x 12				

	D	W	L	THICK	H
FRAME SIZE				5-1/2	10-1/2
PINION GEAR	8	5-1/2			
CRANK DISC	24	2-3/8			
BOILER	60				123

	FLANGE DIA	CORE D/W	GEAR & BRAKE PD	F/ WIDTH	SHAFT DIA
MAIN DRUM	43-1/2	14.5/	48	5-1/2	4-1/2
MAIN BRAKE				8	
H/B DRUM	32	43/	31	5-1/2	4
H/B BRAKE				4	

Sept. 7, 1977

Merv Johnson
Beaverton, Oregon

Dear Sir,

Your letter brings back a lot of memories from 40 to 50 years ago. We always had a yarder and a loader, and sometimes two swing donkeys. We bought our mill from C.C. Keith.

One time my brother Claude was walking along the swing road and his feet got tangled up in some brush. He fell down, and his rear end went down in a hole, while his feet were caught up above. Well, he couldn't move. His caulk shoes were waving in the air while the logs were bouncing over him.

One time I loaned our high climber some money. That was just one of my mistakes, because he left, taking our secretary with him. So I had to climb, top, and rig the next tree. A lot of water has run over the dam.

Yours truly,

Alden Potter

Left   Author's photo of Machine No. 16, 1977.

Right   This photograph's caption reads: "Donkey Engine After the Explosion. River Mill. Ore. 7 Men Killed March 4th, 1911." This is a Vulcan wide face donkey, an early make manufactured in Seattle, Washington.   *Steven Gatke Collection*

Left   Fischer Lumber Company at Marcola, Oregon, around 1907. Marcola is located along the Mohawk River about ten miles northeast of Springfield. This photograph was taken several years before this company had a railroad, so it appears that this road engine was used to bring logs directly to the mill pond.   *Steven Gatke Collection*

Wide Face Donkeys

RESURRECTION

The weathered spar tree looms
    Against the sky,
Circled by fireweed bright
    Against the stumps
That once held rugged lines,
    Now rusty dry.
No noisy Shay grunts up
    The weaving rails
To lead the loaded log cars
    Down the hills.
No whistle punk jerks
    Signals to the man
Who rolls the donkey drums,
    No whistle shrills.

Where are the boots that ripped
    The rugged bark?
Where are the hats that bore
    Their owner's mark?
No lunch pails wait,
    No snoose can etches dirt
Upon the pocket of a hickory shirt.

    Where is Whitey, the climber,
Who rode the sway
    As the mighty giants
Lost their tops?
    Where is John, whose humor
Eased his trying day?
    Where are the choker setters
Who scrambled to safety

Gone. . . .

Yet, look, the trees are rising
    On the hill!
New growth has sealed the raw
    And ugly scars
The rabbits rear their young
    Where all is still.
A fern shoves up its furled
    And twisted head
Through slash and broken
    Bark and rutted land,
And life appears again
    Where all was dead.
In my heart, I know that
    God is kind;
That those who labored
    Here will find
Green slopes to log
    In some far land
Where spirits of those lordly
    Tree will stand,
That God in his great
    And loving grace
Will let them meet again
    In yet another place.

by Peg Hatfield

Drawing from 1925 W.I.S.Co. catalog, pg. 27

In Search of Steam Donkeys

Right This famous photograph shows Yeon & Pelton's 2-spot locomotive moving a small donkey engine to a new location. This 42" gauge engine was one of several Baldwin-built "dummies" that once served street railways in Portland, Oregon. The engineer is Harry Coleman. The purposeful looking fellow standing at front left is John Yeon. *John T. Labbe Collection*

Below This beautiful 1917 photograph shows Palmer Lumber Company's camp on the Walluski River, a tributary of the Youngs River, southeast of Astoria, Oregon. The train at the rollway is headed by their 33-ton Climax locomotive, s/n 1019, built in 1910. *John T. Labbe Collection*

Wide Face Donkeys ·

This is Yeon & Pelton's rollway above Rainier, Oregon. The logs were brought to the loading point by the roading donkey in the background, and then rolled onto the disconnects by hand. These cars have short lengths of rail (roosters) between them. This prevented them from separating during their trip down the incline to the log dump on the Columbia River. Yeon & Pelton built their railroad to 42" (bastard) gauge. Their first locomotives were steam dummies from Portland street railways.   *John T. Labbe Collection from Mrs. Kirk*

In Search of Steam Donkeys

ROAD ENGINES

The term "wide face," used today to describe any donkey with wide drums, is especially applicable to the road donkeys. These were first used on ground lead logging as yarders, road, or swing donkeys. Some skid roads were of the "pole" type; that is, small logs, or poles were used to line the trough. When used as swing donkeys on swing roads, logs were pulled from the yarding area to the loading area. Sometimes more than one swing donkey was used, which created some long hauls before the logs were finally loaded. The drums had considerable cable capacity because of their width. Some roaders were used with high lead systems in which logs were pulled from spar tree to spar tree ; others were used as "incline machines," in which log cars were pulled up or lowered down railroad grades too steep for locomotives. Still others were used with ground lead systems, sometimes using "Tommy Moore" blocks which allowed butt rigging to pass through them.

Above "Tommy Moore" block from Mallory Logging Equipment No. 6. *Glen Comstock Collection*

*N*ARROW drum engines have long been accepted as the best type for yarding purposes, but there is at all times a demand for wide drum machines. We have developed the wide drum engine to the highest possible degree. These Willamette engines represent the latest and best engineering design, and their construction embodies materials of special selection. More steel has been incorporated in their make-up than is found in any other make of similar type logging engine, all the important parts subjected to severe service being made of steel. The boiler has a large diameter and is constructed for a working pressure of 200 pounds. The oblong firebox type is used, and the boiler proportions are such as to insure ample steam capacity throughout the maximum length of haul. The importance of this feature is appreciated by those seeking the most economical results.

Unusually Long Skid Road

Above and right Catalog cuts for "Tandem Drum Road Engines" from 1925 Willamette Iron & Steel Works Catalog. *Glen Comstock Collection*

Tandem Drum Engines

Size	10" x 11"	10" x 13"	11" x 13"
Frame	15" 60-lb. I-beams Length over all, 12' 10" Width over all, 8' 3"	15" 60-lb. I-beams Length over all, 14' 3" Width over all, 8' 8"	15" 60-lb. I-beams Length over all, 15' Width over all, 8' 10"
Drums	Main Drum: 17" dia. 43" long 42" dia. flanges Trip Drum: 15" dia. 43" long 34" dia. flanges	Main Drum: 19" dia. 44" long 46" dia. flanges Trip Drum:* 22" dia. 44" long 40" dia. flanges	Main Drum: 18" dia. 45" long 52" dia. flanges Trip Drum:† 22" dia. 44" long 40" dia. flanges
Capacity	Main: 3000' of 1⅛" Trip: 6900' of ⅝"	Main: 4000' of 1⅛" Trip: 8200' of ⅝"	Main: 5500' of 1⅛" 4500' of 1¼" Trip: 8500' of ⅝"
Gears	Trip, 32" dia. Pinion, 8" dia. Main, 48" dia.	Trip, 38" dia. Pinion, 8.6" dia. Main, 54" dia.	Trip, 38" dia. Pinion, 9.3" dia. Main, 60" dia.
Shafts	Trip, 3⅞" dia. Crank, 4⅛" dia. Main, 4⅜" dia.	Trip, 4⅜" dia. Crank, 4⅜" dia. Main, 4⅞" dia.	Trip, 4⅞" dia. Crank, 4⅜" dia. Main, 5⅜" dia.
Boiler	48"x80" firebox 54" dia. shell 212 2" tubes	53"x80" firebox 60" dia. shell 263 2" tubes	53"x80" firebox 60" dia. shell 263 2" tubes
Speed	Main, 596 F.P.M. Trip, 700 F.P.M.	Main, 507 F.P.M. Trip, 684 F.P.M.	Main, 526 F.P.M. Trip, 733 F.P.M.
Weight	28,000 lbs.	34,200 lbs.	37,000 lbs.

*May also be furnished with a 15" Trip carrying 9,900 ft. of ⅝" or a 28" Trip carrying 6000 ft. of ⅝" line.

†May also be furnished with a 15" Trip carrying 10,000 ft. of ⅝" or a 28" Trip carrying 6100 ft. of ⅝" line.

MACHINE NO. 17

This Willamette wide face is described in the 1925 catalog as a "tandem drum road engine." It is now at Powers, Oregon, care of Coos County Parks and Recreation. These machines could be ordered with a gypsy spool or strawline drum outboard on the main drum shaft. The firebox is single extended type.

The following is from Rolph Hongell of Coos Bay, as told to him by George Rice, crew member:

The wide face steam donkey at Powers, Oregon was brought from Coos Bay Logging Company at the truck logging (Mack chain-drive Bulldogs) camp on Catching Inlet, Coos Bay by Oscar Franz. Daniels Creek C.B., built a new water tank on it and moved three miles through the woods to Daniels Creek to log a "forty." They ran one-inch pipe down a canyon and moved a Fairbanks Morse pump engine there. That was not enough power to raise the water from the creek. A larger engine had to be brought in and assembled below before water could be pumped to the donkey. The crew consisted of George and Grover Rice, Ira Noies, Dave West, and Al McCullough (donkey puncher). The donkey was later moved to the head of Daniels Creek where it sat for years along the Snake Road until moved by the county to Powers Park.

Author's 1978 photo of Machine No. 17 at its present location, in care of Coos County Parks and Recreation, Powers, Oregon.

OWNER Location Builder Type Bore & Stroke	Coos County Parks & Recreation Powers, Oregon Willamette Iron & Steel Works S/N 447 Wide Face Road Engine 10 x 13				Machine #17
	D	W	L	THICK	H
FRAME SIZE		78	192-1/2	15	5-1/2
PINION GEAR	7-1/2	6			
CRANK DISC	25	3-3/4			
FIREBOX	60		84		58-1/2
BOILER	60				134
SMOKEBOX	58				16

	FLANGE DIA	CORE D/W	GEAR & BRAKE PD	F/ WIDTH	SHAFT DIA
MAIN DRUM	44	/44	53-1/2		5
MAIN BRAKE	43			4	
H/B DRUM	40-1/2	20.5/44	37-1/2		4-3/8
H/B BRAKE	34-1/2			3	
STRAW DRUM	27	9/8	(main)	(main)	5
STRAW BRAKE	26-3/4			3	

Additional data:
  Supply pipe - 3"
  Split firebox door

Above Road engine illustration from 1925 W.I.S.Co. catalog. *Glen Comstock Collection*

OWNER	Lulay Bros.				Machine
Location	Private display				#18
Builder	Willamette				
Type	Wide Face Road Engine S/N 320				
Bore & Stroke	11 x 13				

	D	W	L	THICK	H
FRAME SIZE		78	168	5-3/4	14-1/2
PINION GEAR	9-3/8				
CRANK DISC	26	3-1/2			
BOILER	66				124

	FLANGE DIA	CORE D/W	GEAR & BRAKE		SHAFT DIA
			PD	F/ WIDTH	
MAIN DRUM	52	17/45	60		5-3/8
MAIN BRAKE				4	
H/B DRUM	40	13/44	38		4-7/8
H/B BRAKE				2-1/2	

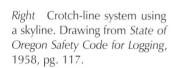

Author's photo of Machine No. 19 at its present location, 1985

Machine No. 18 was shipped new from Willamette Iron & Steel Works on October 15, 1907 to Globe Milling Co. At some point it was converted to "monkey motion" valve motion. Other past owners were: Carlson Cole Lumber Co., U.S. Logging Co. (1916), Western Lumber & Export Co. In 1936 Machine No. 18 was in the possession of Lulay Bros. According to William Lulay, Jr., owner of this machine, this engine was once used for yarding, then used to lower logs to the mill on a short incline railroad. A small railroad car was used at that time to haul mill ends used for firewood from the mill 300 feet up to the donkey.

It was next used as a cold deck machine with 700 feet of skyline and three million board feet capacity using a crotch line system with extra blocks on the carriage and spreader bar. It could pick up an entire load at a time, using straps. The head tree and tail trees were both on hills, which provided ample lift. This operation was near its present location at the Lulay Mill and continued until 1945, when the mill burned. This operation made the cover of the January, 1937 *West Coast Lumberman*, shown on the following page.

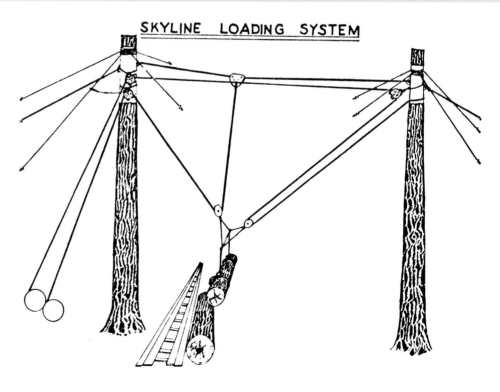

SKYLINE LOADING SYSTEM

Right Crotch-line system using a skyline. Drawing from *State of Oregon Safety Code for Logging*, 1958, pg. 117.

DECKED DOUGLAS FIR LOGS AT A WILLAMETTE VALLEY MILL, PRODUCED DURING LOW COST MONTHS READY FOR WINTER SAWING . . . SEE "LOGGING THE WILLAMETTE VALLEY"

Machine No. 18 in action, out of view but near its present location, made the cover of the January 1937 *West Coast Lumberman* (a forerunner of the present day *Forest Industries*). The magazine also included a follow-up story on the Lulay operation.   *Oregon Historical Society Collection, permission from Forest Industries, Miller Freeman Publications*

OWNER Location Builder Type Bore & Stroke	Columbia County Historical Society Vernonia, Oregon Washington Iron Works Hoisting Engine s/n 1787 no cylinders				Machine #19
	D	**W**	**L**	**THICK**	**H**
FRAME SIZE		49-1/2	104	4	varies
PINION GEAR	6	4			
FIREBOX	48				48
BOILER	48				116
SMOKEBOX	43				28
	FLANGE DIA	**CORE D/W**	**GEAR & BRAKE PD F/ WIDTH**		**SHAFT DIA**
MAIN DRUM	25-1/2	13/24	28	3-1/2	3
MAIN BRAKE	25-1/2			4	
H/B DRUM	25-1/2	13/24	28	3-1/2	3
H/B BRAKE	25-1/2			4	

Author's photo of Machine No. 19 at the Columbia County Historical Society Museum, Vernonia, Oregon, 1992

This donkey was assembled from a Washington Iron Works industrial hoist and a boiler used in a mint still. Mr. Hamilton, the one who donated the boiler, has indicated that the boiler was used in a donkey by a logging company at Clatskanie Heights at one time. Bob Eastman of Mist, Oregon donated the Washington Iron Works hoist. The hoist was owned by a company that bought it Army surplus and converted it to internal combustion power. The company changed names several times over the years, from J&H/Allied, to Olympic Forest Products, and then to R.S.G. Mills. Stanley Matthews made some changes and prepared the equipment for delivery to the museum.

MACHINE NO. 20

Right Another example of what a "donkey hunt" can lead to. Faced with the choice of clearing blackberry vines or being late for my next appointment, I opted to be on time. The blackberry vines, made it impossible to photograph as is. There is in fact a 2-drum 4 x 9 American Hoist & Derrick industrial hoist under those vines. It was hard to get any measurements in the briers, but we found that the drum gears were 30", the pinion was 6-1/2 ", all with a 4" face. The drum cores are 12" diameter x 28" wide. The boiler is 48" diameter by 108" tall. This machine was used at Coos Head Pulp Mill in the 1950s as a dragline to clean a log slip. Piling was used as a tail hold. It hasn't been used since. It is owned by Danny Hongell (left in photo), son of Rolph Hongell, who is mentioned with the Coos Bay vertical Spool donkey (No. 2). John Deveraux (at right) transported me to this site in a 1940 Chevy pickup!
Author's photo circa 1989

Wide Face Donkeys

Above Machine No. 21, a Washington Iron Works donkey, was used at the first mill owned by George and Frank Overholzer, circa 1928. The donkey is in the house at the right in the photograph. *Photo from Ross Overholzer*

Left Photo by the author of Machine No. 21at its present location, 1992.

OWNER	Ross Overholzer				Machine
Location	Private display				#21
Builder	Washington Iron Works				
Type	Wide face yarder s/n 608				
Bore & Stroke	9 x 10				

	D	W	L	THICK	H
FRAME SIZE		60	137	varies	5
PINION GEAR	7	6			
CRANK DISC	20	2			
BOILER	48				96

	FLANGE DIA	CORE D/W	GEAR & BRAKE PD	F/ WIDTH	SHAFT DIA
MAIN DRUM	34	11/28	47	4	4
MAIN BRAKE	32				
H/B DRUM	30	11/28	42.5/4	4	3-1/2
H/B BRAKE	26				

This single-drum donkey is mounted on a sled built in the early 1990s at a museum being set up at Blue River, Oregon by owner Dave Knapp. The only name we could find on the machine is "O&S." It came from Shelton, Washington. No other information is available. *Author's photo, 1992*

OWNER Location Builder Type Bore & Stroke	Dave Knapp Blue River Oregon Unknown (Stamped "O&S") Wide Face Single Drum 5 x 7				Machine #22
	D	**W**	**L**	**THICK**	**H**
FRAME SIZE		43	58	3	7-1/2
PINION GEAR	5-1/2	3			
CRANK DISC	14	1-3/4			
BOILER	28				72
SMOKEBOX	20				9
	FLANGE DIA	**CORE D/W**	**GEAR & BRAKE** **PD**	**F/ WIDTH**	**SHAFT DIA**
MAIN DRUM	27	8/17	24-1/2	2-1/2	2-1/2
MAIN BRAKE	23			2-1/4	

Right Wide face Tacoma yarder circa 1939. This is the donkey S & L Chapman used for most of their logging. Being lighter than the Smith & Watson[7] made it easier to move around. Glen Philips in the picture. Photo by Nellie (Chapman) Phillips near Yoncalla, Oregon on the Phillips Ranch. *Courtesy Nellie Phillips.*

7 See story on page 92

Wide Face Donkeys

Machine No. 23

Above Machine No. 23 in Milwaukie, Oregon. *Philip Schnell photo, 1996.*

OWNER Location Builder Type Bore & Stroke	Al Foglio Milwaukie, Oregon American Hoist & Derrick Hoisting Engine 5-1/2 x 7				Machine #23
	D	**W**	**L**	**THICK**	**H**
FRAME SIZE		41-1/2	77	8	4
PINION GEAR	26	4			
CRANK DISC	18	2-1/2			
FIREBOX	30				28
BOILER	30				72
SMOKEBOX	22				
	FLANGE DIA	**CORE D/W**	**GEAR & BRAKE PD F/ WIDTH**		**SHAFT DIA**
MAIN DRUM	21	10/20.5	27-1/2	3-1/2	2-1/2
MAIN BRAKE	21			2-1/2	
H/B DRUM	21	10/20.5	27-1/2	3-1/2	2-1/2
H/B BRAKE	21			2-1/2	
GYPSY (REAR)	12/8-1/2	6/8			
GYPSY (FRONT)	11	5-3/4/10			

This American Hoist & Derrick is neatly installed on wheels as a self-propelled crane. It features reversing valve gear (eccentrics) plus two gypsies. It came from the state of Wisconsin, where it had been mounted as it is now. Owner Al Foglio has a small museum which displays a variety of mechanical artifacts, including an FWD snowplow, snow cats, trucks, a locomotive, and a crazy-looking Model-T Ford used to clown-around in parades.

Machine No. 24

Above Machine No. 24, in its current location. *Author's photo, 1995*

OWNER Location Builder Type Bore & Stroke	Loren Wilton Private Display American Hoist & Derrick Hoisting Engine 7 x 10				Machine #24
	D	**W**	**L**	**THICK**	**H**
FRAME SIZE		50	84		varies
PINION GEAR	5	4-1/2			
CRANK DISC	20	2-1/4			
FIREBOX	36				24
BOILER	36				84
	FLANGE DIA	**CORE D/W**	**GEAR & BRAKE PD F/ WIDTH**		**SHAFT DIA**
MAIN DRUM	20	/22	25/4	4	3
MAIN BRAKE	27			3	
H/B DRUM	25	/24	25.5/4	4	3
H/B BRAKE	25			3	

This American Hoist & Derrick is hiding in the woods near a farm. It was converted to an internal combustion engine, but fortunately, the cylinders and some of the linkage are still there. This is another machine with a vague history. It is known that it was used in approximately 1917, and again for the last time in 1941 or 1942, by Albert Graff at its present location.

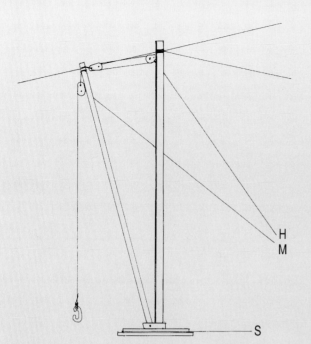

OWNER Location Builder Type Bore & Stroke	Camp 18 Logging Museum Elsie, Oregon Clyde Hoisting Engine S/Ns 5204 & 5401 10 x 12				Machines #25 & # 26
	D	**W**	**L**	**THICK**	**H**
FRAME SIZE		71	117	6	12-3/4
PINION GEAR	7	5			
CRANK DISC	25	2-3/4			
BOILER	54				108
	FLANGE DIA	**CORE D/W**	**GEAR & BRAKE** **PD**	**F/ WIDTH**	**SHAFT DIA**
MAIN DRUM	34	19/38	36/5	5	4-1/2
MAIN BRAKE	34			5	
H/B DRUM	34	19/38	36/5	5	4-1/2
H/B BRAKE	34			5	

Above   This drawing is similar to the derricks used at Wilkenson Quarry. At "H" is the drum line used to raise and lower the boom. "M" is the drum line used to pick up the granite and lower it below. "S" is the cable leading to the slewing engine, which turns the derrick.   *Author's drawing*

Above   Machine No. 25 on display at Camp 18 Logging Museum near Elsie, Oregon.   *Author's photo.*

Left   Machine No. 26 on display at Camp 18 Logging Museum.   *Author's photos, 1995.*

These industrial hoists were two of four steam hoists that we discovered on one of our "wild donkey hunts" in 1989 at Wilkenson Granite Quarry near Buckley, Washington. They had shut down the operation prior to our visit, but we were able to see how they had been used. They were rigged to a rotating mast with boom attached. The boom and mast rotated together via an auxiliary swing winch (also called a slewing engine) with reversing gear. As the raw granite was blasted loose from the cliff, it was lowered to the mill below. Granite was supplied to the Washington State Capitol, among other destinations .

John Taubeneck reports that the factory in Duluth, Minnesota shows both being shipped to Clyde Equipment Co. of Seattle on July 1, 1922. Where they went from Seattle when new is not known, but we know that Wilkenson Quarry shows S/N 5401 in operation on or before June of 1958. S/N 5204 was put into operation at the quarry on February 17, 1964. The hoists are identical, except for the boilers, which have been removed. One boiler now at Camp 18 Museum is a welded boiler with an unusually small firebox door. Small firebox doors evolved when crude oil came into use because a large door (for wood) wasn't necessary. This door, however, is unusually small. These two machines were moved to Camp 18 Museum in the early 1990s.

MOVING DAY

Kerry Timber Company, 1917, near Nehalem Camp, above Kerry, Oregon. The drama of donkey moves such as this was captured in Clark Kinsey's historic photographs. Working in the highball camps was hard, backbreaking work; the rigging men were fast movers, and the logs and rigging were large, but they hired enough men to do it, according to Lee Johnson, engineer on this donkey (more names on request).

The "spring pole" at front extending above the house, was used to maintain tension on the whistle wire. Note the stick in the eye of the haulback line to hold tension with the "bullseye" type fairlead. The mainline (men holding the bight) and haulback fairleads were mounted on top of the ample-sized head block. On this sled, the strawline went through the head block. The haulback drums on these Willamette compounds (Humboldts) were offset, necessitating separate fairleads. When tree rigged, it was necessary to thread the haulback through the fairlead en route to the high-lead block to maintain lead when spooling on the drum. While I cannot attest to the durability of this particular mainline fairlead, this photograph reminds me of one that flew apart when moving donkey. It flew apart with the hook-tender standing in the bight next to it. He lived, but was seriously crippled for life and lost an arm.   *C. Kinsey photo from Steven Gatke Collection*

In Search of Steam Donkeys

Chapter 3
Compound Geared Yarders
(and a few others)

As high-lead logging evolved, donkeys were developed especially for high-lead logging shows. Engine speeds increased, drums became narrow and deep. Gearing became more complicated to provide greater speed ranges and deliver power to more drums needed with high-lead systems.

Willamette Iron and Steel Company explained the reason for compound (intermediate) gearing as a solution to the problem of providing a greater range of speeds not possible on direct geared machines. These developments resulted in capabilities of high gear ratios of more than double that of low gear.* The Willamettes were compounded by using internal gearing.

* W.I.S.Co. 1925 Catalog, pp. 31,32,33,38

In this writer's experience, finding secluded donkeys often begins with a rumor. Most of these stories are like hearing about a lost treasure; One would like to believe it, but most are just rumors. Those machines that have been abandoned in the woods have been there a long time. Forty years is a minimum number of years for this situation today. Many were abandoned in 1929. Chances are, there is not much left because the scrappers have had a long time to pick the woods clean. It is highly probable that any donkey found now was in poor mechanical condition the last day it was used. Why else would it have been abandoned? I remember one that was abandoned near the headwaters of Jordan Creek because it got away from the crew when they were moving it down a hill. Fortunately, the woods are not completely void of donkeys. With a little help from a lot of friends, this search for steam donkeys has become a directory of reality.

People made this varied and intriguing search for steam logging equipment happen. Once in the 1970s I drove up to a trailer court office and asked for the man who was on the crew years ago of one of the donkeys in this book. After a time, he came to the door in a wheelchair. "Yes, I remember it." His face lit up as he reminisced about the old days. "Of course the Willamettes were high production machines, but there was a Smith and Watson up this canyon that could out-log them all." I was trying to imagine this wheelchair victim in stagged-off square-cut jeans and suspenders with hickory shirt, wearing caulk shoes laced up during a time of proud and robust men. He named off some of the crew members but suddenly changed the subject.

"You a writer?" Before I could find the right words he said, "I got a story for you if you want to write it."

"Oh?"

"I know how we can beat the Russians."

"Yeah, how?"

"With bugs. Want to write it? I sent a letter to the president, but he didn't reply."

"Well, I guess not."

Although it is sometimes difficult to stay on the subject, these interviews have ended up with stories of how it once was in the era of the "big woods," much unlike today. The people of course, make the search more interesting. A long trek to a normally inaccessible spot is a thrill, especially when something is found. Machine No. 28, for example, was in one of those places. Lo and behold - a Humboldt yarder, mostly intact! I could not have been more delighted to find a treasure chest in that part of the Oregon Coast Range. As with others, the history on this one is vague. Many times, people who could have helped have died or moved away. Upon checking maps and logging companies, John Labbe has indicated it may have been there since the 30s. That one was unusual for the fact that most of its original parts were still intact. Most donkeys abandoned in the woods have been scavenged to the extent that there is little left.

Compound gears on the Smith and Watson yarder at Douglas County Museum (Machine No. 31). Lee Johnson photo.

North Bend Overhead Logging System

*T*HE North Bend system of skyline logging is in very extensive use throughout the Northwest. This is probably due to the fact that it does not require the use of any special type yarder for successful operation.

The carriage travels on the fixed standing line. It has no out-haul line attached to it. The in-haul or skidding line is fastened to the base of the carriage, passes through a fall block, thence through a head block on the spar tree to the engine. By means of the haul-back line the fall block and the bight of the skidding line are carried into the woods. The carriage, floating on the standing line, comes to rest at a position opposite and above the log, being hooked to the fall block. Upon pulling in the skidding line the load has a constant tendency to raise up at the forward end and thus avoid obstructions. It is a very efficient means of yarding or swinging where conditions are favorable.

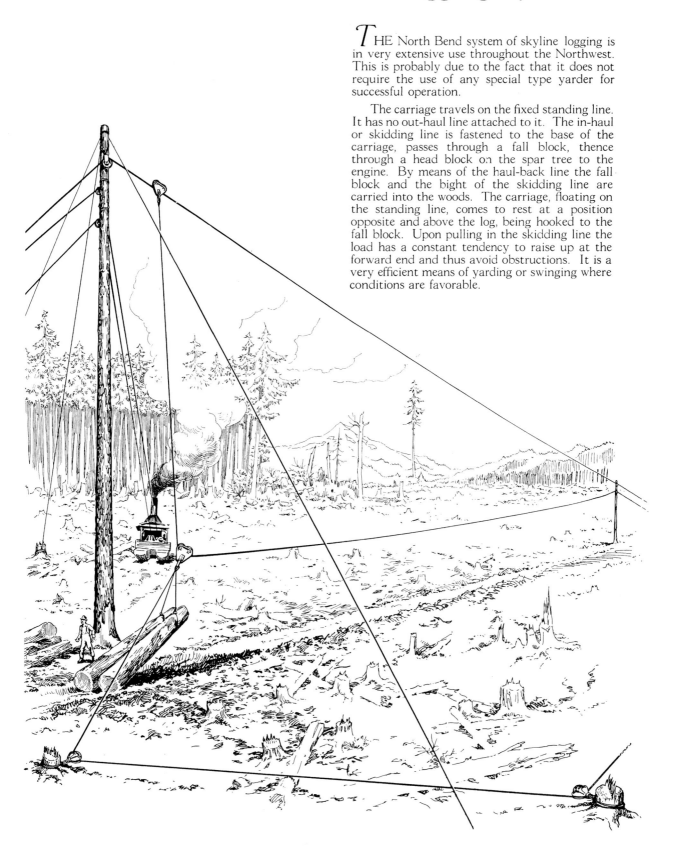

The "North Bend" system shown is one example of how logs were lifted on one end while yarding to reduce obstructions. *1925 W.I.S.C.O. catalog, Pg. 67, Glen Comstock collection*

Another donkey moving view; An Oregon-American Lumber Company Humboldt compound-geared yarder, possibly a two-speed. The contraption on the head block on the other side is a bulls-eye fairlead, used to ensure proper lead for the haulback line. The larger fairlead in the middle was used to direct the mainline to the drum when used for donkey moving. When high-lead yarding, the mainline would pass instead through the slot in the roof up to the bull block at the top of the spar tree. Note the pile of pipe that will be used to supply water for the boiler. Also, notice how one sled runner has been repaired with light cable.   *C. Kinsey photo, Philip Schnell Collection*

In Search of Steam Donkeys

OWNER	Jack Himebaugh				Machine
Location	private display				#27
Builder	Willamette				
Type	Humboldt Yarder S/N 1811				
Bore & Stroke	11 x 13				

	D	W	L	THICK	H
FRAME SIZE		83	192		
PINION GEAR	14				
CRANK DISC	30	3-5/8			
BOILER	60				132
SMOKEBOX	58				

	FLANGE DIA	CORE D/W	GEAR & BRAKE PD	F/ WIDTH	SHAFT DIA
MAIN DRUM	61	32/15	56	4-1/2	5-1/4
H/B DRUM	43	17/31	40		5-1/4
STRAW DRUM	24	13/16			5-1/4

Additional data:
Steam supply pipe - 3"
Pinion shaft - 4-3/4"

Above This Willamette Humboldt yarder was used by Winchester Bay Lumber Company as a yarder, near Reedsport, Oregon, near its present location, until about 1933. According to C.A. Himebaugh, Cliff Tucker was a fireman on it. As can be seen in the photograph, it suffered fire damage when the field in which it stands burned. This engine is believed to be S/N 1811, manufactured in 1920. *Author's photo, 1978*

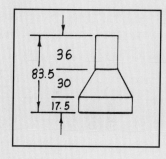

Left Humboldt yarder illustration from 1925 Willamette Iron & Steel Catalog. *Glen Comstock Collection*

Compound Geared Yarders

The
Humboldt
Yarder

The compounding of the gearing of a logging engine has long been accepted as the most natural method of securing the proper relation between the main and haul-back drums in regard to their speed and pulling power.

A close inspection of the special construction of the "Humboldt" Yarder will reveal many desirable features not attained in other compound geared yarders, but all very important in producing results. A powerful pulling main-line drum, a high speed haul-back drum, and a large capacity straw-line drum, are compactly assembled, so when pulling, the cable coils over the top of them, which means that they all rotate in the same direction, at the same time the engine runs over, as it should.

Operator's side of Humboldt yarder.

Humboldt Yarder illustration from 1925 W.I.S.Co. catalog. *Glen Comstock collection.*

HUMBOLDT YARDER
TABLE OF SPECIFICATIONS

SIZE	10" x 11"	11" x 13"***	11" x 13" Special**	12" x 14"	12"x14" Special	13"x14"
FRAME	15" 60-lb. I-beams Length over all, 13' 6" Width over all, 8' 3"	15" 60-lb. I-beams Length over all, 15' 0" Width over all, 9' 2¼"	15" 60-lb. I-beams Length over all, 15' 0" Width over all, 9' 2¼"	18" 70-lb. I-beams Length over all, 15' 3" Width over all, 9' 10"	18" 70-lb. I-beams Length over all, 15' 3" Width over all, 9' 10"	18" 70-lb. I-beams Length over all, 17' 5" Width over all, 9' 10"
DRUMS	Main Drum: 25" dia. bbl., 11¾" long 58" dia flanges Trip Drum: 16" dia. bbl. 13" long 44" dia. flanges	Main Drum: 34" dia. bbl. 14½" long 60" dia flanges Trip Drum: 18" dia. bbl. 13½" long 46" dia. flanges	Main Drum: 34" dia. bbl. 14½" long 60" dia. flanges Trip Drum: 18" dia. bbl. 13½" long 46" dia. flanges	Main Drum:† 36" dia. bbl. 16" long 68" dia. flanges Trip Drum: 24" dia. bbl. 14" long 54" dia. flanges	Main Drum:* 42" dia. bbl. 16" long 68" dia. flanges Trip Drum: 24" dia. bbl. 14" long 54" dia. flanges	Main Drum: 36" dia. bbl. 16" long 68" dia. flanges Trip Drum: 24" dia. bbl. 14" long 54" dia. flanges
CAPACITY	Main, 1700 ft. 1⅛" Trip, 3700 ft. ⅝" Straw, 3700 ft. $\frac{7}{16}$"	Main, 1500 ft. 1¼" Trip, 4050 ft. ⅝" Straw, 4000 ft. $\frac{5}{16}$"	Main, 1500 ft. 1¼" Trip, 4050 ft. ⅝" Straw, 4000 ft. $\frac{5}{16}$"	Main, 1850 ft. 1⅜" Trip, 5500 ft. ⅝" Straw, 5500 ft. $\frac{5}{16}$"	Main, 1900 ft. 1¼" Trip, 5500 ft. ⅝" Straw, 5500 ft. $\frac{5}{16}$"	Main, 1850 ft. 1⅜" Trip, 3800 ft. ¾" Straw, 5500 ft. $\frac{7}{16}$"
GEARS	Pinion, 12" dia. Trip, 38.8" dia. Pinion, 12¼" dia. Main, 50.8" dia.	Pinion, 12" dia. Trip, 40" dia. Pinion, 13.4" dia. Main, 52" dia.	Pinion, 14.3" dia. Trip, 40" dia. Pinion, 13.4" dia. Main, 52" dia.	Pinion, 12.7" dia. Trip, 50" dia. Pinion, 15¼" dia. Main, 57¼" dia.	Pinion, 14.6" dia. Trip, 50" dia. Pinion, 15¼" dia. Main, 57¼" dia.	Pinion, 17.33" dia. Trip, 48.66" dia. Pinion, 15.28" dia. Main, 57.3" dia.
SHAFTS	Crank, 4⅛" dia. Trip, 5⅜" dia. Main, 4⅛" dia.	Crank, 4⅞" dia. Trip, 5⅞" dia. Main, 5⅜" dia.	Crank, 4⅞" dia. Trip, 5⅞" dia. Main, 5⅜" dia.	Crank, 4⅞" dia. Trip, 6⅜" dia. Main, 5⅞" dia.	Crank, 4⅞" dia. Trip, 6⅜" dia. Main, 5⅞" dia.	Crank, 5⅜" dia. Trip, 6⅜" dia. Main, 5⅞" dia.
BOILER	48½"x80¾" firebox 54" dia. shell 212 2" tubes	53½"x80½" firebox 60" dia. shell 263 2" tubes	53½"x80½" firebox 60" dia. shell 263 2" tubes	60½"x90½" firebox 66" dia. shell 341 2" tubes	60½"x90½" firebox 66" dia. shell 341 2" tubes	65½"x90" firebox 72" dia. shell 391 2" tubes
SPEED	Main, 355 ft. per min. Trip, 1058 ft. per min.	Main, 345 ft. per min. Trip, 926 ft. per min.	Main, 410 ft. per min. Trip, 1104 ft. per min.	Main, 316 ft. per min. Trip, 886 ft. per min.	Main, 365 ft. per min. Trip, 1027 ft. per min.	Main, 440 ft. per min. Trip, 1240 ft. per min.
WEIGHT	38,700 lbs.	45,000 lbs.	45,000 lbs.	56,000 lbs.	56,000 lbs.	59,500 lbs.

Author's note: Extant machines seldom match all these dimensions exactly, because of the various manufacturer's combinations and options. This is not a list of the only Humboldt yarders available.

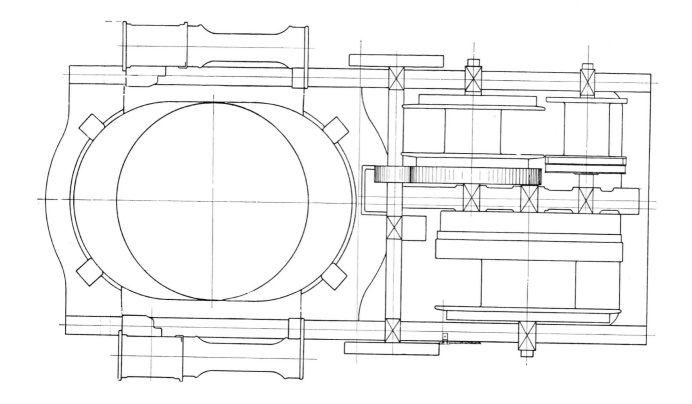

Compound Geared Yarders

MACHINE NO. 28

Above Machine No. 28 deep in the Tillamook Forest, with considerable help from my friends: John Birdeno, front left, and Bill Creech led me to this one. The other two are Homer Simmons and grandson, Tracy Schlaeppi. *Author's photo, 1979*

Right Photograph taken of the author on Machine No. 28 in 1979. Donkey hunters found an extra crank disc (29-1/2" Dia. x 13" stroke) on ground nearby. A donkey hunt in the Tillamook Forest with amazing results! *Author's photo, 1979*

Additional data:
 Steam supply - 3-1/2"
 Exhaust pipe - 3-1/2"
 Pinion shaft - 4-1/2"
 Boiler brace rod - 2"
 Firebox Door - 17 x 12-1/2
 Smokebox extension - 16"
 Funnel height - 30"
 Smokestack height- 27"

The Willamette internal gear.

Above Humboldt yarder illustration from 1925 W.I.S.Co. catalog. *Glen Comstock Collection*

OWNER Location Builder Type Bore & Stroke	State Department of Forestry Salmonberry Canyon (in Oregon's Coast Range) Willamette Iron & Steel Works Humboldt Yarder s/n 928 11 x 13				Machine #28
	D	W	L	THICK	H
FRAME SIZE		78	177	5-3/4	15
PINION GEAR	10-3/4	5			
CRANK DISC	26	3-3/4			
BOILER	60				124-1/2
	FLANGE DIA	CORE D/W	GEAR & BRAKE PD	F/ WIDTH	SHAFT DIA
MAIN DRUM **MAIN BRAKE**	60 63	30/14	45	6-1/2 2-1/2	5-3/4
H/B DRUM **H/B BRAKE**	46 35	/10-1/2	40	5 2-1/2	5-3/4

LONG-LOST DONKEY REVISITED

Aug 26, 1995: Your author couldn't be sure we would find it, not having been there since 1979, so we embarked on an exploratory "unofficial" donkey hunt. A long trek into a remote area of the Coast Range of Oregon (along the Salmonberry Canyon near Belding) revealed the Humboldt yarder still hiding in the brush. The machine hadn't changed much since our 1979 pilgrimage. Trees are still growing, a few more parts are missing, and a little more rust has developed. We found what we were looking for, took pictures, made more measurements, and headed back on the long, arduous task of climbing out of one of the deeper canyons in the Coast Range.

George Martin, of the Oregon State Department of Forestry, has come to a reasonable conclusion regarding the history of this machine. We have asked ourselves over the years, why is this machine there? It is not a place where donkeys were normally found. There is no sign of a landing or other logging activity one would expect to find. We observed damage caused by a shaft being torn from the machine. There are extra parts on the ground nearby and signs of babitt bearings being poured.

Following a lead on a story regarding a fire and work attempted on the donkey, George put some information together. He noted one patch of timber to the north that was not logged in 1932. His theory is that the donkey was brought in from below on the Southern Pacific Railroad, and was being moved uphill under its own power when it was damaged. It appears that they were in the process of making repairs with the extra parts and pouring new bearings when a local fire occurred in October of 1932. The green timber to the north was probably the destination, but the fire caused them to give up.

Although Willamette sales records files do not give much information on these early engines which would help in more positive identification, we know that West Oregon Lumber Company was in possession of an identical machine numbered S/N 928 in August of 1911. Also shown in the records is Coats Driving and Boom Co. owning or doing work on S/N 928 in 1915, and in a few years following. We also know that West Oregon logged on or near the present site during the years George Martin mentioned.

Below Three determined donkey measurers hard at work! Left to right: Phil Schnell, Merv Johnson, Wally Sarpola *Photo by Robert Wenzel, 1995*

Above Across the canyon from the donkey below, Ken Smjekel (4th from left) took us to a vantage point to chart our course. From left to right: Bob Wenzel, Phil Schnell, Fred Wenzel, (Ken) Joanne Hastings, Ralph Swan, Wally Sarpola.

Below We found it! *Both photos by the author, August, 1995*

This dramatic 1925 photograph captures The Whitney Company logging a sawtooth ridge in the rugged Coast Range above Idaville, Oregon. This is their well-remembered "Blue Star" camp. Whitney operated a large sawmill at Garibaldi, Oregon. *Russell Hawkins photo, courtesy of Dorian Studio of Tillamook, Ore.*

Right What a way to treat a brand-new steam donkey! This mishap occurred on Connacher Logging Company's operation out of Vernonia, Oregon. The Willamette engine does not appear to be seriously damaged.
Lee Johnson Collection

Below This view shows a factory-fresh Willamette compound geared two-speed yarder just before being placed on its sled. This was at Nehalem Timber & Logging Company out of Scapoose, Oregon.
C. Kinsey photograph, Martin E. Hansen Collection

Compound Geared Yarders

Above This photo was taken by Rolph Hongell before Machine No. 29 was moved to the Bohemia Lumber Company shop in Eugene, Oregon and dismantled. It has since been scrapped. That's Rolph standing with the yarder.

engine with cylinders 10 inches in diameter or larger. The first extended fireboxes were not unique to the Humboldt. An article in a 1911 edition of *The Timberman* notes that "two extended firebox boilers were built recently at the urging of A.W. Clark, of O.K. Logging Co. of Marshland, *(later became Coos Bay, ed.)* Oregon. One was used by Oregon Timber and Lumber Co. in Clifton, Oregon, and the other one went to Saginaw Lumber Co. in Aberdeen, Washington."

OWNER Location Builder Type Bore & Stroke	Bohemia, Inc. Eugene, Oregon (scrapped) Willamette Humboldt Yarder c/n 1082 11 x 13				Machine #29
	D	W	L	THICK	H
FRAME SIZE		78	192		
PINION GEAR	12				
CRANK DISC	30				
BOILER	60		90		58
SMOKEBOX	30				
	FLANGE DIA	CORE D/W	GEAR & BRAKE PD F/ WIDTH		SHAFT DIA
MAIN DRUM	60		52		5-3/8
H/B DRUM	46		40		5-7/8
STRAW DRUM	16		11		

The Humboldt yarder was the forerunner of a new era of high-production machines, and was the basic design for many models that followed. In particular, the High-Speed and the Two-Speed compound yarders had their beginnings with the Humboldt. The Humboldts were readily adapted to highlead logging. Willamette apparently sold more Humboldt yarders than any other type. Engine records suggest that the first was manufactured in 1906 (s/n 219). Willamette continued building them until the mid-1920s, although by this time the purchase of a new Humboldt was rare, with the increased power, speed, and other improvements of the newer models. Internal gearing tended to hold the shafts together (so the company claimed). One of the Humboldt "Specials" was the High-Speed, which was simply a Humboldt with faster gears. It proved itself as a high-production "log getter" for certain types of shows.

Extended firebox boilers were first offered by Willamette beginning in 1911. This type of boiler provided a much larger heating surface, while keeping the boiler's width the same. It also allowed a larger fire to be built, and longer pieces of fuel would fit in the firebox. These boilers subsequently became so popular that in 1912 over 90% of all the engines manufactured that year by Willamette had extended (oblong) fireboxes. Willamette offered this type of boiler on any

```
Dear Mr. Johnson:

    Relative to your inquiry regarding the 11 x 13
Willamette Humboldt yarder at Horton, it was
purchased by Hult Lumber Company in
approximately 1936 (ed.—W.I.S.Co. records
suggest 1946). It had belonged to a contract
logger named Harry Swartz who logged in the
upper Lake Creek country in the early 30s. He
went broke in the Depression as did so many and
the yarder was repossessed by Alaska Junk
Company in Portland . . . We bought it from
them. According to my records it carries serial
No. 1082. We used it primarily for high lead
logging as we had very large old growth timber,
and as you know, the Humboldt was designed to
log Redwood, being very slow but powerful on the
mainline, and the compound geared haulback gave
it a lot of speed going back to the brush. The
machine was just as it came out of the
Willamette shop. As far as I know no
modifications were made. It did not have a
bleeder valve.
    It was last used as a cold deck machine in
1946.

Nils B. Hult
```

Above This information was provided by a previous owner of Machine No. 29.

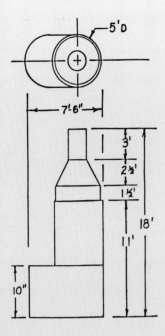

Above   Machine No. 29 at the Bohemia Lumber Company shop, 1977. *Photo by the author*

Additional data:
Boiler - single extended type
Pressure on nameplate - 265/175 lb.

The photograph below was taken by Bill Hudson in the 1970s.

Some information in the Willamette Iron & Steel records:

1913	Campbell Logging Co. Delivered new by barge
1935	Ingram Bros.
1935	Smith Bros.
	Columbia Logging Co.
	H.B. & A. Logging Co.
1946	Hult Lumber Co.

Sad to say, this machine was scrapped in the 1980s. A home can usually be found for these irreplaceable relics. Do what you can to save the donkeys!

Donkeys had been worth more than scrap value for a generation before this machine was needlessly scrapped. A machine in restorable condition such as No. 29, had a market value of two to three times its scrap value. Museums have been begging for (tax deductible) donations such as this donkey. It is hoped that this book will raise public awareness and help to prevent such unnecessary tragedies in the future.

Steven R. Gatke

Above and right   Machine No. 30 is in "kit" form. It is located in a remote area of the Oregon Coast Range. As is the case with most of these abandoned donkeys, they are incomplete and difficult to get out. I was led to this donkey by Ken Smejkal, upper left, and Bill Harkson, upper right, his son, below. Rich Hobart, lower right.   *1979, Merv Johnson*

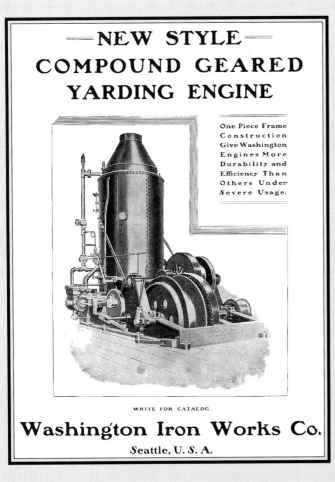

Ad from January, 1907 *Timberman. Tim Anderson collection*

Additional data:
Stack diameter - 29"

OWNER	Unknown				Machine
Location	Salmonberry Canyon, Coast Range				#30
Builder	Washington Iron Works				
Type	Compound Geared Yarder				
Bore & Stroke	12 x 12				

	D	W	L	THICK	H
FRAME SIZE		77-1/2	180		
PINION GEAR	11-1/2				
BOILER	72				120

	FLANGE DIA	CORE D/W	GEAR & BRAKE PD F/ WIDTH		SHAFT DIA
MAIN DRUM	60	/26			
MAIN BRAKE	3				
H/B DRUM	42-1/2	21			
H/B BRAKE	2-1/2				

THE HUNT FOR A LOST DONKEY

by Jenelle Wiggins

The Oregon woods hold a lot of surprises and this spring Stanley Mathews of Mist, Oregon and Ken Smejkal of Vernonia, Oregon found one in the shape of a 12 x 12 Washington compound yarder.

An alert hunter, scouring the Salmonberry country for elk, was probably the first to stumble upon the old donkey, and by word of mouth the story of its existence spread. Sometime back Ken Smejkal had heard of the abandoned machine and went with friend Bill Harkson to investigate. They found the donkey alright, nestled on a hillside among fir trees and vine maples near the ghost logging town of Belding, Oregon. The men marveled at the machine and tried to imagine it in its heyday, with the fire box stoked, steam up and a hard pull on.

Anyone who has ever logged with a steam donkey has also fought it, cursed it, kicked it, and in general got the whole business under his skin. Stanley Mathews is one such man. Stanley and his brothers ran the Mathews Brothers Logging Company from 1920 through 1948, and during most of those 28 years in the woods they depended on steam for power. When the wood ran out in '48 the Mathews' shut down their mill and Stanley has busied himself with welding and fabrication since then. But some days that steam still seems to flow through his veins. When rumor of the abandoned steam donkey reached Stanley's ears his curiosity was sparked. The damp spring weather held him off a few weeks but with the first prospect of clear skies, Stanley and friend Ken Smejkal were in the pickup and on their way to have a look-see.

It was an arduous ride in 4-wheel drive down a steep, winding, boulder strewn road into the heart of the Salmonberry country. As the pickup lurched and bounced along, Stanley pointed out wildlife and recalled the "good old days" of logging. At the bottom of the canyon the men parked the truck and got out, following the railroad track for a mile or so on foot.

To a logger the woods can read like a city street with a burnt snag or stump representing alleys and intersections in the forest. For Ken, a trickle of water indicated a sharp left turn and up the hill they climbed and then back down a ravine. "I hope I can remember where it is," Ken muttered out loud. "Maybe it would be best if you waited here while I look over the next ridge," he said and headed off.

Stanley leaned on his walking stick. "You know," he said with a deadpan face, "if one leg's longer than the other, a person will walk in circles and get lost." A scrub jay in a nearby tree laughed at that one. "The best thing that could happen is we'd find a 12 x 14 Willamette yarder," he mused in anticipation. "The worst thing that could happen is if it turned out to be like one I owned. In 1906 they made the first 2-drum donkey. Before that they used a 1-drum or spool donkey. It took 10 square feet of heat to make 1 horsepower." A shout of "Over here! I've found it!" rose above the mist as Stanley spoke, and off he went across the ridge at a fast clip.

When he caught sight of the donkey, Stanley broke into a grin. "Well, it's better than I thought, but not as good as I hoped," he wise cracked. "It's a compound yarder, a 12 x 12 Washington with a quad-riveted butt strap boiler, 10 feet 4 inches long and 60 inches across I'd say just to look at it." "Seventy-two inches across," he corrected himself.

"It's an old timer," he continued, pointing to the cast iron frame. "The first donkeys were cast and later on they used steel. This donkey has been badly stripped. It has no sled plates and no shaft. There should be two of them, one to run the haul back and one to run the main gear. It weighed around 7 tons and had 400 horsepower and in a hard pull could break a 1-3/8 inch main line. I think it broke down and they just left it."

"From the looks of it this was just a gyppo outfit," he went on. "They probably yarded the logs to here and then another donkey yarded the logs down to the railroad. What you'd call a two-donkey show." A notch in a stump caught Stanley's eye. "That notch was used to keep the line straight in a corner," he explained. "That's known as an Oregon lead."

Stanley critically examined the yarder making sure no important detail had gone unnoticed. Fully satisfied he turned to go, intent now on reaching the lunch box in the front seat of the pickup, and the sooner the better.

Reprinted from "Locals Find Steam Donkey in Woods," an article appearing in *The Vernonia Freedom*, Summer, 1980. Vernonia, Oregon

MACHINE NO. 31

This type is billed in the Smith & Watson catalog No. 9 as a "Universal Yarding Engine - Two Speed." This and the "Convertible" yarder were often called "sledge hammer" two-speeds because of the sometimes difficult method of sliding the pinion gear over to change speed. These were designed with the intention of changing the gear according to the type of logging encountered, e.g., large/small timber or ground/skyline logging. The con-

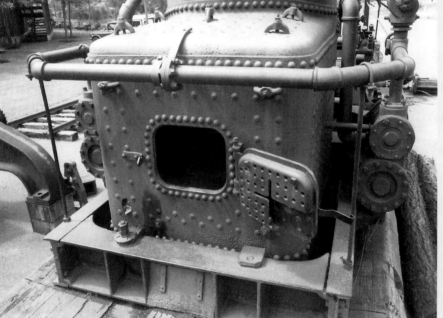

Photos this page   Machine No. 31 at its present location at the Douglas County Museum in Roseburg, Oregon, right off I-5. Author's photos, 1978

vertible yarder was equipped with a skyline drum and seemingly different two-speed ratios than the "Universal."

These were the forerunners of the more sophisticated two-speeds which Washington Iron Works and Willamette Iron and Steel built. The boiler was perhaps one of the better features of the Smith & Watson yarders, in which they had overcome the obstacles of the rectangular firebox design.

OWNER	Douglas County Museum	Machine
Location	Roseburg, Oregon	#31
Builder	Smith & Watson Iron Works	
Type	Compound Geared Two-Speed Yarder	
Bore & Stroke	11 x 13	

	D	W	L	THICK	H
FRAME SIZE		86	202-1/2	6	15
MAIN PINION GEAR, HIGH	11-1/2	7			
MAIN PINION GEAR, LOW	10-1/2	7			
PINION GEAR, HAULBACK	16	6			
PINION GEAR, INTERMEDIATE	24	4			
CRANK DISC	27	3-1/2			
FIREBOX			94		55
BOILER	60				
SMOKEBOX	60				

	FLANGE DIA	CORE D/W	GEAR & BRAKE PD	F/ WIDTH	SHAFT DIA
MAIN DRUM	54	28/17	57/6.5	4	6
MAIN BRAKE	52			4	
H/B DRUM	45	19/13.5	37/5.5	2-1/2	5-1/2
H/B BRAKE	34			2-1/2	
STRAW DRUM	MISSING				4
GYPSY	16/17	11.5/11	STRAW		*

* Gypsey is mounted on intermediate shaft

Engine plate drawing of Machine No. 31 by Bill Roy

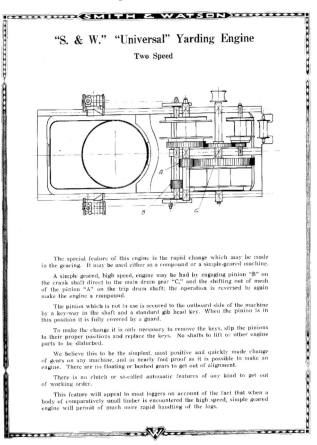

"S. & W." Compound Geared "Universal" Yarder

Two Speed — 11″ x 13″

This type of engine is furnished with round or extended firebox boiler.
All gears are cast steel, machine cut, true to pitch.
Valves are of our well-known balanced piston type. Valve operating gear is of the monkey motion type. Oil pump, "Manzel" force feed.
Main and trip drums are equipped with our "S. & W." self-aligning, ball-bearing friction devices.

Specifications

FRAME—15″-60-lb. "I" beams; 14′-1″ long; 9′-6¼″ wide, over all.
BOILER—Round; 68″ diameter, 144″ high; 313-2″ tubes, 7′ long.
GEARS AND PINIONS—Main, 57″ diameter, 6½″ face; main pinion, high, 10″ diameter, 7″ face; main pinion, low, 12″ diameter, 7″ face; Trip, 39″ diameter, 5½″ face; trip pinion, 16″ diameter, 6″ face.
DRUMS—Main, composite, 51″ flanges, 28″ barrel, 17″ long; capacity, 1500′-1¼″ line; Trip, 48″ flanges, 20″ barrel, 13″ long; capacity, 4100′-¾″ line; Straw, 28″ flanges, 12″ barrel, 13″ long; capacity 3850′-⅜″ line.
SHAFTS—Main, 5¾″ diameter; Trip, 5¾″ diameter; Straw, 3⅞″ diameter; Crank, 4⅜″ diameter.
Line speeds: Main, high, 680 feet; main, low, 425 feet; Trip, 1080 feet.
Engine speed, 350 R. P. M.

Two pages from Catalog No. 9 of the Smith & Watson Iron Works of Portland, Oregon. *Author's collection, date unknown.*

"S. & W." "Universal" Yarding Engine

Two Speed

The special feature of this engine is the rapid change which may be made in the gearing. It may be used either as a compound or a simple-geared machine.

A simple geared, high speed, engine may be had by engaging pinion "B" on the crank shaft direct to the main drum gear "C," and the shifting out of mesh of the pinion "A" on the trip drum shaft; the operation is reversed to again make the engine a compound.

The pinion which is not in use is secured to the outboard side of the machine by a key-way in the shaft and a standard gib head key. When the pinion is in this position it is fully covered by a guard.

To make the change it is only necessary to remove the keys, slip the pinions to their proper positions and replace the keys. No shafts to lift or other engine parts to be disturbed.

We believe this to be the simplest, most positive and quickly made change of gears on any machine, and as nearly fool proof as it is possible to make an engine. There are no floating or bushed gears to get out of alignment.

There is no clutch or so-called automatic features of any kind to get out of working order.

This feature will appeal to most loggers on account of the fact that when a body of comparatively small timber is encountered the high speed, simple geared engine will permit of much more rapid handling of the logs.

A PERSONAL ACCOUNT OF MACHINE NO. 31

Reminiscing with Nellie (Chapman) and Hershel Phillips, they recall:

Hershel:

"I worked on the crew as a riggin' man, and punked whistle. Some of the other crew were Les Chapman (owner), Orval Long, Ralph Long, and Clare Chapman. We used 3/4" haulback, the mainline was about 1-1/4". We now have a museum at Yoncalla, and we like to reminisce about old times."

Nellie:

"I was hired to work in the cookhouse. This was near Billy Creek, about 1935, which is in the Drain-Skelley area. Previous to the Billy Creek operation, the donkey was at Divide which is south of Cottage Grove.

Clare and I recall when Bohemia Lumber Co. was owned by William Garoutte and La Sells Stewart. They were finishing their operations on Martin Creek 2-1/2 miles from Highway 99 and 7 miles from Cottage Grove, Oregon, in the thirties. Most of the equipment had been moved to Culp Creek but the Smith & Watson had been left and the rails used to let logs down to the pond at the sawmill site.

My brothers, Sherman and Leslie, removed the rails and hauled them to Highway 99 for which they received the Smith & Watson for their efforts. They moved the donkey to the Frank Chapman ranch (our father) where they used it to clear land. This ranching was adjacent to Bohemia's operation.

The next move was to Skelley, west of Yoncalla and Drain to the Harold Phillips ranch. The donkey was moved on the old Reo truck in pieces and reassembled. It was used the first summer to log Barn Canyon. From then on, this donkey was used in winter only. As they logged Middle Canyon on Billy Creek, plank road followed to haul logs to the mill.

This was a small operation. The crew usually consisted of a donkey puncher, riggin' slinger, and a whistle punk. Wood to fire the donkey was slab wood hauled from the mill. The donkey puncher fired the boiler.

Some of the donkey punchers we recall through the years were Clare, Sherman, and Leslie Chapman, Bill Hoskins, Curley Gordon and Clarence Ash. Other employees were Orval and Ralph Long, Linn Chapman, Harold and Herschel Phillips. Jim Mackey, a timber faller of yore, and Ralph Long often worked together.

We had another donkey, a Tacoma, which we called "Old Bets." My older brother, Clare was fond of saying Old Bets had a friend called "Maude," another donkey. Old Bets was used to log on Wards Butte as a swing yarder. When Sherman and Leslie finished the Wards Butte setting and moved to Skelley in 1934, Old Bets was incorporated into the mill. The boiler was set up separately to power the mill. The drums were used to pull logs into the mill. The mill was sold to Dick Zelkie in 1946. At that time, Old Bets was still part of it.

I too whistle punked, but years later using an electric "bug." That was for two brothers in Alaska. I stood on a tiny stump and I wear number 10s. Try to imagine me with so many rain clothes on I could hardly wiggle.

The most beautiful sight in the world! In August I looked down on beautiful Prince William Sound, greeted black bears, saw eagles on high and ducks below. Our nearest neighbors were thirty miles by water only. This was later the epicenter of the quake.

When I was a kid, my brother Linn and I spent a lot of time in the sawmill. Our dad was the sawyer, and he insisted we sit down. Mom used to say: 'shut the door, were you born in a sawmill?' Well, we might as well have been, or maybe on a hillside where the doors swing shut.'

Above   Machine No. 31 when in service by S & L Chapman Brothers at head of middle fork of Billy Creek - Skelley area out of Yoncalla, Oregon. Some crew members were: Herschel Phillips, Harold Spence Phillips and Glenn Phillips (both standing in shadow).

Below   S & L Chapman sawmill on the Phillips Ranch at Skelley, Oregon sometime in the late 30s or early 40s.
Both photos by Nellie (Chapman) Phillips.

Compound Geared Yarders

The following information is from the Douglas County Museum in Roseburg, Oregon, which is the present location of this donkey:

This Smith & Watson steam logging donkey was manufactured in Portland, Oregon about 75 years ago. It was first used in a logging operation in the Cottage Grove area* and also in land-clearing around Divide.

Sherman and Leslie Chapman, brothers, acquired the machine and moved it to their S. & L. Chapman logging operation on Billy Creek in the Skelley area southeast of Drain, Oregon. The operation closed in 1936, and the sawmill was removed; the old steam donkey was left standing in the woods at the side of the last loading landing where it was used.

The road leading to the site crossed over the mill dam, and this dam washed out, preventing the donkey from falling into the hands of scrap dealers during World War II. Leslie Chapman, one of the partners, passed away; and Sherman Chapman of Drain, the surviving partner, deeded the donkey to the Douglas County Museum in 1968, but due to lack of a road the old relic remained in the woods. Later the Bureau of Land Management had a timber sale in the site area and a new access road was built, allowing the County Road Department to move the donkey to the museum. The original wooden sled had decayed to such an extent that only the metal machine parts were recovered. Mr. Martin Sowa donated a used donkey sled made from large logs, and the donkey was sandblasted, painted and mounted on the wooden sled on a concrete base in the museum yard for permanent display. The old relic is a memorial to the old-time loggers and the days when steam was king of the woods.

* According to an article by Steven Gatke in TimberTimes, issue No. 2, Spring 1993, this yarder was purchased by the Chapman Brothers from the Leona Mills Lumber Co. of Leona, Oregon.

Left This photo, courtesy of the Douglas County Museum, was taken near the Chapman Mill on Billy Creek, previous to its final move to the Douglas County Museum in Roseburg, Oregon. Sherman Chapman is in photo.

A Smith & Watson 12 x 13 convertible yarder at the factory. This machine is similar to No. 31 in this book. Because of the drum arrangement which caused secondary drums to turn in the opposite direction from the main drum, Smith & Watson used one or more rollers on the front of the frame to keep lines from these "undershot" drums from rubbing against the frame members. *Angelus Studios, from collection of Doug Warneke*

Compound Geared Yarders

MACHINE No. 32

Above Machine No. 32 at its present location in Dallas, Oregon. *John Tucker photo, 1988*

Smith & Watson Iron Works originated in 1862 in Portland, Oregon. Records show a name change to General Iron & Steel Works in November 1934, with Alfred E. Smith as owner.

Bill Ames of Falls City, Oregon provided the history of Machine No. 32: This machine was first used as a yarder at Black Rock, Oregon by the Willamette Valley Lumber Company. It was later displaced by skidder logging and was used as a cold deck machine, still at Black Rock. Remaining with the same company, it was next used as a decking machine at the mill in Dallas, then later as a reload machine. It was displaced again by a railroad locomotive crane which did the decking along the tracks. Eventually the boiler was removed, but the machine was kept in service, supplied by mill steam, used for cleaning the pond there.

Additional data:
    Haulback pinion: 8″ wide x 19″ P.D.
    Roller:
       core: 7-1/2″ x 16″
       flanges: 11″
       Shaft: 2-3/8″

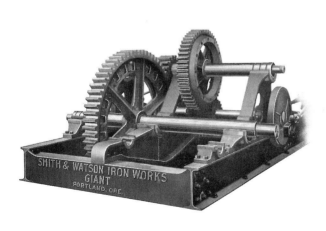

This cut from the Smith & Watson catalog No. 9 shows the compound gear arrangement. *Author's collection*

OWNER	Willamette Industries				Machine
Location	Dallas, Oregon				#32
Builder	Smith & Watson Iron Works				
Type	Compound Geared Two-Speed Yarder				
Bore & Stroke	11 x 13				

	D	W	L	THICK	H
FRAME SIZE		90	200		
PINION GEAR	12-1/2	6			
CRANK DISC	29-1/2	3-1/2			

	FLANGE DIA	CORE D/W	GEAR & BRAKE PD	F/ WIDTH	SHAFT DIA
MAIN DRUM	60	34/14	62	7-1/2	6.5
MAIN BRAKE	50				
H/B DRUM	46	19/14	40	6	6-3/4
H/B BRAKE	39				
STRAW DRUM	36	28/26			
STRAW BRAKE	27				

In Search of Steam Donkeys

A Smith & Watson donkey similar to Machine No. 32 on the facing page. Note the enormous spark arrestor. Location and date unknown. *Chris Horlyck collection*

MACHINE NO. 33

M
achine No. 33, a Humboldt yarder built by Willamette Iron & Steel Works has been resting silently for years in a remote area of the Oregon Coast Range. A future move and cosmetic restoration effort is a possibility. The spar tree last used with the donkey is still standing nearby. The idea of leaving such marketable timber in the woods seems incredible in our contemporary world, but there was no way of loading a spar tree once the rigging was removed. There still remain other spar trees standing in various parts of the Oregon Coast Range.

Quinn Murk led us to this machine. It was not easy to get to the old landing. We chose the shortest route, which meant wading through brush thick as the hair on a dog's back. On this donkey hunt were Mike Boell, Ralph Swan, Quinn Murk, and the author. According to Quinn, this was a three-donkey haul, with this machine used as the middle swing yarder. The other two donkeys were easily accessible to scrap, but this machine was another story. Quinn had heard that the scrappers had tried to move the donkey with two cats, but only succeeded in getting it out of plumb. The plans to scrap it were then abandoned, leaving it in partially dismantled condition. Hutchinson Timber Company appears to be the last company to have logged with this machine. Their operations were shut down in 1936. The property has changed hands over the years, and is now owned by Boise-Cascade Corporation.

Above Machine No. 33 at its present location in the Oregon Coast Range. Examination of Willamette Iron & Steel records indicates that this is probably s/n 1497. *Photo by author, 1989*

Below Donkey hunt participants savoring their find of Machine No. 33—left to right: Quinn Murk, Ralph Swan, Mike Boell, Merv Johnson. *Photo by Mike Boell, 1979*

Additional data:
    Throttle valve - 3-1/2"
    Pinion shaft - 5"   Wt. - 56,000 lb.
    Single extended firebox   Chunking drum - misc.
    Firebox Door - 16-1/2 W x 20 H   uses, yarding firewood, etc.

OWNER Location Builder Type Bore & Stroke	Boise-Cascade Corp. Oregon Coast Range Willamette Iron & Steel Works S/N 1497 Compound Geared (Humboldt) Yarder 12 x 14				Machine #33
	D	W	L	THICK	H
FRAME SIZE		88	192+	5-3/4	18
PINION GEAR	15-1/4	6			
CRANK DISC	30	3-1/4			
FIREBOX	66		99		
BOILER	66				140
	FLANGE DIA	CORE D/W	GEAR & BRAKE PD	F/ WIDTH	SHAFT DIA
MAIN DRUM	68	42/16	57-1/4	6-1/2	5-1/2
MAIN BRAKE	68			3	
H/B DRUM	54	29/14	50	6-1/2	5-1/2
H/B BRAKE				4	
STRAW DRUM	36	16/6	15	5-1/8	5
STRAW BRAKE	31			2	
CHUNK DRUM	24	13/21-1/2	15	5-1/8	5
CHUNK BRAKE	24			3	

In Search of Steam Donkeys

Above   An Oregon-American Lumber Company Willamette "Humboldt" yarder, mounted on a giant sled. Notice how it hangs over the ends of the Seattle Car & Foundry moving car. Also interesting is the tank car in the background with the large hose reel, and the bull block lying on the sled. This was a very typical scene during the steam era in Western Oregon.   C. Kinsey photograph, Martin E. Hansen Collection

Compound Geared Yarders   101

BENSON TIMBER COMPANY

Both photographs on this page are by Clark Kinsey at Benson Timber Company near Clatskanie, Oregon.

Left   Note the lack of coats in spite of a snow logging show. This Humboldt yarder sports a square metal tank which was unusual, but the dilapidated sheet metal house was common.

Bottom   Note the use of roller fairleads and the holes and hardware in the sled to accommodate straps.

Both photographs courtesy of Rudolph Larson

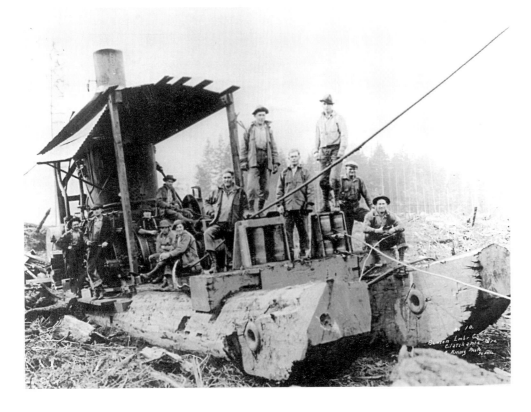

WINTER LOGGING

Right Winter logging, C.H. Wheeler Lumber Company at Cochran, Oregon. A Willamette interlocking skidder with wooden spar tree. A sight of bygone days showing three and six log loads and with the spar tree partially obscured by steam. *From Jack Taylor W.I.S.Co. Collection*

GIANT SIMPLEX YARDER

Bottom John Cummings photographed this Washington Iron Works 13 x 18 yarder owned by Western Logging Company of Valsetz, Oregon. According to John, it was previously used by C.D. Johnson. This appears to be the same machine that Byron Ames operated and maintained in 1935. Byron was a yarder engineer and donkey "doctor" for Cobbs and Mitchell. This is the largest size simplex yarder listed in the Washington Iron Works catalog. Although this yarder is large by any standards, Bert Pickens of Forest Grove has informed us of a Washington slacker with two 13 x 14 engines used at Camp 12 out of Siletz, Oregon at the C.D. Johnson Company. This machine is similar to the machine now on display at Scotia, California. It used a 2-inch skyline, a 1-3/8 inch skidding line and 1-1/8 inch haulback (or receding) line. Bert relates nine million board feet in one month when he worked there. *John Cummings photo, 1959*

T hanks to Ron Greenwood and his son, one more obscure donkey is written into history. In the bottom of a canyon, it is not easy to find, nor to move out.

Additional information: 69 foot sled
3" steam supply pipe

Below   A P.S.I.&S.W. "Tacoma" compound-geared yarder catalog illustration of a machine similar in size to Machine No. 34. *Mallory Catalog No. 6, Glen Comstock collection.*

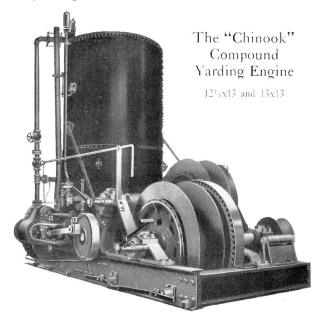

The "Chinook"
Compound
Yarding Engine

12¹⁄₂x13 and 13x13

OWNER Location Builder Type Bore & Stroke	Sparrow & Crow Oregon Coast Range Puget Sound Iron & Steel Works Compound Geared Yarder 11-1/2 x 13				Machine #34
	D	W	L	THICK	H
FRAME SIZE		84	172	6-1/2	15
PINION GEAR	13-1/2	6			
CRANK DISC	26	3-3/4			
FIREBOX	64				60
BOILER	64				120
	FLANGE DIA	CORE D/W	GEAR & BRAKE PD F/ WIDTH		SHAFT DIA
MAIN DRUM	54	30.5/15	53-1/2	6	6-1/4
MAIN BRAKE	26			3	
H/B DRUM	44	18/15	39	5-1/2	5-3/4
H/B BRAKE	36			2-1/2	
STRAW DRUM	21	11.5/21.5	22-1/2	6	
STRAW BRAKE	20				
GYPSY	20.5/22.5	15/12.5			

A Basic High-lead System

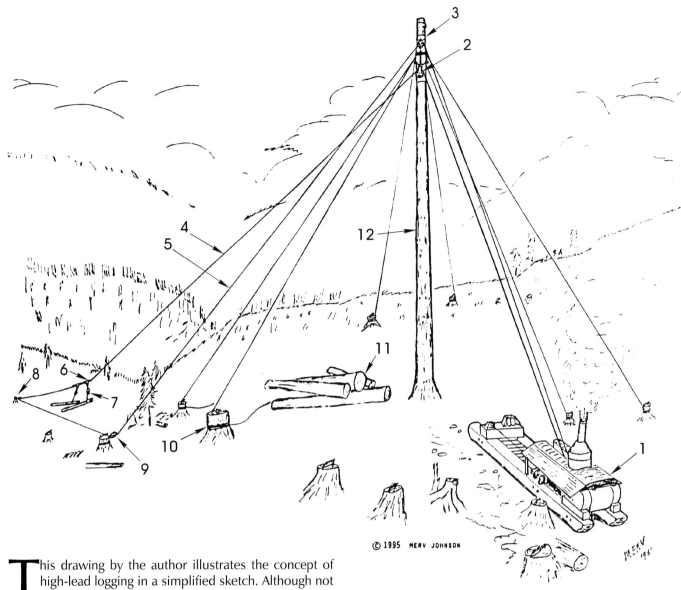

© 1995 MERV JOHNSON

This drawing by the author illustrates the concept of high-lead logging in a simplified sketch. Although not intended to be a guide for rigging, it depicts the main idea. While slow to catch on, high-lead logging was suddenly popularized in 1916. As it evolved, methods were developed to make it safe and reliable. Over the years, much more complicated aerial yarding systems came into being, but the high-lead system was the most common. It is still used today, steel towers having replaced the wooden spar tree.

With few exceptions, another set of guylines (called buckle guys) were required. Missing also, is some indication of the destination of these logs. Sometimes logs were 'decked' into a pile and left to be moved later, as shown here; the usual situation at this site would be either another donkey "swinging" logs off this pile to another location, or this tree would be rigged for loading to a railroad or trucks. It is also important to note the necessity of having a third drum, called the "strawline." Look closely on the yarder, left front of the sled, and the small cable can be seen. It will be used when it is time to move the lines to another skid road.

1. Yarder (sled-mounted)
2. Bull block for the mainline
3. Haulback block
4. Mainline
5. Haulback
6. Butt-rigging
7. Chokers (two shown here)
8. Tailhold and tail block
9. Corner block
10. Guyline and stump (six required, usually three wraps and spiked)
11. Log deck
12. Spar tree (commonly 190 ft. high in Coast Range of Northwest Oregon)

Two-Speed Yarding in Retrospect

The Willamette Two-Speed yarder became the answer to many loggers' desire for high production. A successor to both the Humboldt (low geared) and the Willamette High-Speed yarder, it incorporated both speed and power. Extended fireboxes provided ample steam and, in fact, sometimes boiler safety valves popped-off when the turn of logs was coming in!*

Steam donkeys are probably best remembered for their speed and power, even though it took a lot of fuel to achieve both. Some were oil burners, of course, but a lot of wood was also burned in order to maintain the supremacy of steam. It was not uncommon to have two cutters (also called "wood bucks") plus a fireman. It is hard today to imagine three or more cords of thirty-nine inch straight-grained wood per day going up in smoke.

Although Willamette built six types of two-speed yarders, there were only two basic differences between each type. After considerable experimenting, Willamette settled into production with the direct-geared and the compound-geared configurations. The direct-geared type was simply a large gear on one side of the main drum, and a smaller gear on the other side. This was sometimes called a "simple-geared" yarder. The compound geared yarder used a self-contained unit, separate, but connected to the main drum with internal gears (see page 111). This gear arrangement had its be-ginnings with the Humboldt yarder. In fact, this type of two-speed yarder was sometimes referred to in sales literature as "Humboldt Two-Speed Yarder." The compound-geared two-speed yarder provided smooth shifting on the move, and of the 332 two-speed machines sold, 57 were the early experimental type, 153 were the final compound-geared design, 95 were direct-geared, and the remaining 27 were miscellaneous types, including lowering machines and "units."

Who would have thought at the time that anyone could ever improve on such advanced technology! Indeed, as times changed, diesel yarders were eventually built to equal the production of the late model steam giants of the highball days of logging. What the early internal combustion donkeys lacked in power and reliability was made up by less weight and lower labor costs. Many of the large steam donkeys of the high-lead logging era were scrapped on site in the woods as the timber ran out, and then carried away in pieces. This explains why so few of the steam giants are around today to testify to a vanishing era.

The last Willamette Two-Speed yarder to operate in Oregon may have been at Long-Bell's operation near Vernonia, in 1957. There was talk of saving it, but true to form, it was scrapped on site. Jack Easter was the engineer. (See pages 114 and 115.)

---

* According to the late Lee Johnson, yarder engineer, a wood-fired donkey with a large firebox sometimes would "pop" on the way in because the fire at that time of the cycle developed a bed of hot coals, creating more than adequate heat. Of course, exceptions occurred in the form of long hauls, mechanical condition, etc. I remember seeing a tube sheet in such poor condition that when the firebox door was opened, it was literally raining inside! This was during the last days of one operation.

WILLAMETTE COMPOUND TWO-SPEED YARDER

This view shows a Willamette Iron & Steel Works compound-geared two-speed yarder, s/n 2415, at Nehalem Timber and Logging, Scapoose, Oregon, in February of 1926. The tanks on the rear of such machines were for water and/or crude oil. This is a wood burner, but if it were an oil burner, the tank would have a partition at about 2/3 of its length, the smaller portion for oil, and the larger for water. A "hit and miss" gasoline-engine pump would be piped to transfer water from the nearest source to the tank. This pump would be left running all day.

This 12 x 14 yarder was equipped with piston valves, and a steam "jam" on the main drum. In time, steel water/oil tanks became common. This early wooden tank is in contrast with this contemporary compound geared two-speed with piston valves and a guard over the cross head barrel. Note the iron pipe across the left front side of the house about four feet up. This kept the strawline up and out of the way when slack. The strawline drum on these machines was on the haulback shaft, which helped to keep it up some, but when slack, it tended to rub on the two-speed unit guard. This is another reason for large, high head-blocks (cross member) on the front of the sled, which together with fairleaders mounted on them, kept the lines up and in lead with the drums. Note the marlin spike and other tools on the deck. When it came time to move, the deck would often be loaded with rigging from the site. *Photograph courtesy of Oregon Historical Society, WISCO collection photo #2922*

Compound Geared Yarders

MACHINE NO. 35

OWNER	Camp 18 Logging Museum	Machine
Location	Elsie, Oregon	#35
Builder	Willamette Iron & Steel Works s/n 2343	
Type	Compound Geared Two-Speed Yarder	
Bore & Stroke	12 x 14	

	D	W	L	THICK	H
FRAME SIZE		88	252	6	18
PINION GEAR					
CRANK DISC	30	3-1/2			
FIREBOX		75	96		75
BOILER	75				159
SMOKEBOX	75				24

	FLANGE DIA	CORE D/W	GEAR & BRAKE PD	F/ WIDTH	SHAFT DIA
MAIN DRUM	72	36/17.5	60-1/2	6	6
MAIN BRAKE	72			3-1/4	
H/B DRUM	54	24/15.5	42	5-1/2	5-1/2
H/B BRAKE	53-1/2			6	
STRAW DRUM	35	20/11	42	5-1/2	5
STRAW BRAKE	34-1/2			2-1/4	

	KEY	P.D.	F/WIDTH		
CRANK PINION (HIGH)	H	20	8		
CRANK PINION (LOW)	L	11	8		
FINAL DRIVE TO MAIN DRUM	FD	18	6		
2-SPEED UNIT	A	42	6		
2-SPEED UNIT	B	50	6		

Additional data:
  Crankshaft - 4-1/2" Dia.
  Steam friction on main and 2-speed unit
  Hand friction on haulback and straw-line
  Piston rod - 2" Dia.
  Draft door - 7-1/2" x 45"
  Frame boiler cavity - 74-1/2" x 100"

Above   This factory builder's photo shows the right hand (engineer's) side of Machine No. 35 just before delivery. Note the guards installed over the cross head guide, gears, steam frictions, as well as the familiar crank disk guard. The distinctive blue and white "Willamette" plate was bolted onto this guard on each side.   *Oregon Historical Society, W.I.S.Co. Collection, No. 2876*

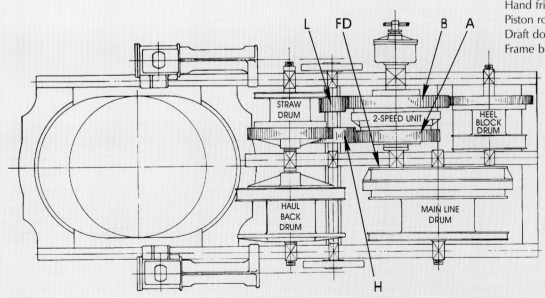

Machine No. 35 at Camp 18 Logging Museum near Elsie, Oregon. *Philip Schnell photo, 1995*

HENRY J. NEWMAN SAVED THIS ONE

A good news story. We are fortunate that Henry J. Newman and his wife, Florence, once owned Machine No. 35. Both were fond of this two-speed yarder. After selling it, Henry later learned that it was about to be scrapped. Because of their fondness for the machine, Henry and Florence bought it back from the scrapper. After Henry died, Florence held on to it until Maury Clark and Gordon Smith of Camp 18 Logging Museum became interested in it. A former Clark & Wilson Lumber Co. machine, it was a welcome addition to the museum, whose many displays are reminiscent of the Clark & Wilson Lumber Company. This machine now boasts a new sled, house, and a boiler from Milwaukie, Oregon. Stanley Mathews overhauled the hoist, and Dean Smith built the sled. It awaits boiler overhaul.

From the Willamette Iron & Steel records:

This machine (S/N 2343) was shipped to Nehalem Timber & Logging Co. of Scapoose, Oregon on 11/7/25 on N.P. car #60894. It was originally equipped with a 72" extended firebox boiler (#11006).

Clark & Wilson Lumber Co. of Scapoose, Oregon appears to have been the next owner of this machine, when they absorbed Nehalem Timber & Logging Co. sometime in the 1930s. When Clark & Wilson sold out, Newman & Svoboda acquired it for their logging operation at Scapoose, Oregon in the early 1940s. From there it went to its present location at Camp 18, around 1987.

These Willamette two-speed yarders were popular machines, used during the heyday of steam logging. Unfortunately, very few have escaped the scrapper's torch. We've been unable to locate any others in Oregon and we are aware of only one in Washington State, and two or three in California.

With its new spar tree raised nearby, it is hoped that Machine No. 35 will eventually become a working reminder of the age of steam logging!

Compound Geared Yarders

TWO-SPEED YARDER — COMPOUND GEARED

fast in high gear as in low. The change is accomplished instantaneously at full speed of the engine without any racking, jarring or undue strain on any part of the equipment or rigging.

Many substantial improvements over previous logging engine design have been incorporated in the construction of this machine. The trip drum shaft is located behind the crank shaft. It is driven by the same pinion as the high gear, with the result that the highest speed yet found practical to use is obtained. The trip drum is located immediately behind and directly in line with the main drum. The trip drum shaft is supported by a center bearing. A large capacity straw line drum is mounted on the opposite side of the high speed shaft, from the trip line drum. All controls for the straw drum are carried to the right hand side, affording the operator full control of all drums of the engine. A feature of this machine is that all drums are equipped with unusually large diameter, broad face, testbestos lined, brake bands. Brake bands are sufficiently large to permit of snubbing the load with trip drum on skylines and handling the log at the spar tree with main drum, without the necessity of slipping frictions. More steel is incorporated in the construction of this engine than any previous models,

it being literally an all-steel machine. All gearing, drums and bearings on the engine are annealed cast steel. The main drum is of the composite type, built up with cast steel flanges and semi-steel barrel, firmly bound together with nickel steel bolts. All gears in the engine have accurate machine cut teeth. Special equipment is used to cut the teeth of the internal gear, made necessary by the speed of rotation in high gear. This improvement has tended to greatly reduce the vibration and frictional losses, thus reducing the wear and tear in the engine.

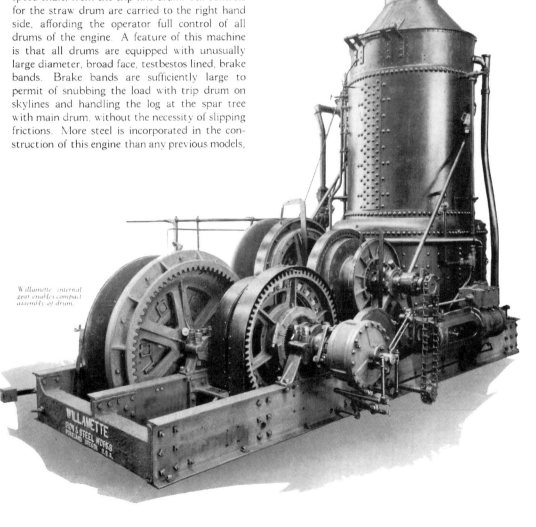

Willamette internal gear enables compact assembly of drum.

This page, illustrating the compound-geared two-speed yarder, is taken from the Willamette Iron & Steel Works catalog for 1925, pg. 33. *Glen Comstock collection*

In Search of Steam Donkeys

WILLAMETTE IRON AND STEEL WORKS

TWO-SPEED YARDER—DIRECT GEARED

threaded on the shaft at both ends of the drum absorb the thrust and prevent drum from moving laterally on the shaft. The main drum gears are likewise equipped with extremely heavy brass bushings.

The wide variety of logging conditions in the timbered areas of the West Coast has necessitated the building of direct geared two-speed engines in several sizes, with reference to speed and power, as well as line capacity.

The lighter machines are particularly well adapted for short high lead yarding in light timber or for operating skyline swings.

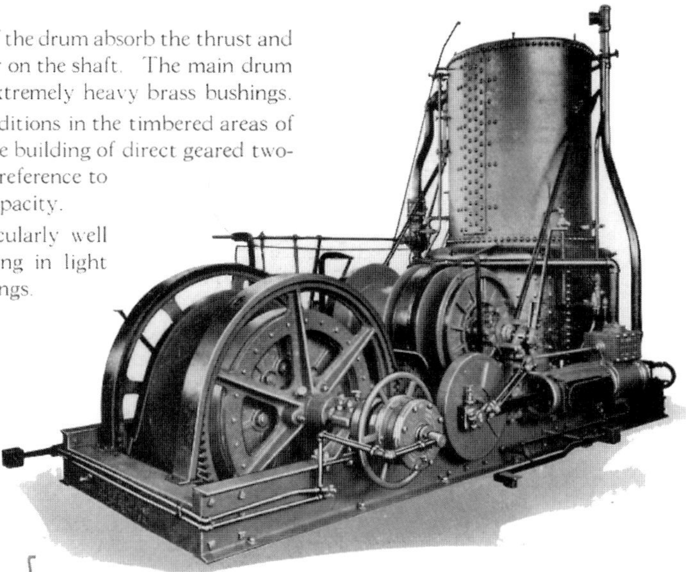

TABLE OF SIZES

Size	Frame	Drums	Capacity	Speed F. P. M.	Shafts. Dia.	Boiler	Weight
11"x13"	15" 60-lb. I-beams. Length over all: 19' 4" Width over all: 9' 2"	Main: 24" bbl. 24" long. 48" dia. flanges Trip: 26" bbl. 24" long 42" dia. flanges Straw: 20" bbl. 8" long 40" dia. flanges	Main: 2150' 1⅛" Trip: 4400' ⅝" Straw: 4500' ⅜"	Main: Low 427 High 762 Trip 1280 Straw 1170	Main 5⅜" Trip 4⅞" Crank 4⅞"	53"x80" firebox. 60" dia. shell 261 2" tubes	51,000 lbs.
12"x14"	15" 60-lb. I-beams Length over all: 20' 3" Width over all: 9' 5"	Main: 24" bbl. 24" long 54" dia. flanges Trip: 26" bbl. 24" long 42" dia. flanges Straw: 20 bbl. 8" long 40" dia. flanges	Main: 2900' 1⅛" 2354' 1¼" Trip: 4400' ⅝" Straw: 4500' ⅜"	Main: Low 430 High Trip 1230 Straw 1085	Main 5⅜" Trip 4⅞" Crank 4⅞"	60"x90" firebox 66" dia. shell 354 2" tubes	54,000 lbs
13"x14"	18" 70-lb. I-beams Length over all: 20' 9" Width over all: 10' 0"	Main: 30" bbl. 24" long 66" dia. flanges Trip: 30" bbl. 24" long 52" dia. flanges Straw: 30" bbl. 7½" long 46" dia. flanges	Main: 3500' 1¼" 2900' 1⅜" Trip: 5000' ¾" Straw: 4250' ⅜"	Main: Low 529 High 944 Trip 1283 Straw 1156	Main 6⅞" Trip 5⅞" Crank 5⅜"	60"x90" firebox 66" dia. shell 354 2" tubes	62,000 lbs.

All above machines can be equipped with an Oversize Boiler.

This page, illustrating the direct-geared two-speed yarder, is taken from the Willamette Iron & Steel Works catalog for 1925, pg. 38. *Glen Comstock collection*

Above Kerry Timber Company, 1917. This was an early two-speed yarder design built by Willamette, Lee Johnson at the throttle. *From the Lee Johnson collection.*

Below This view shows a late model Willamette two-speed yarder built specifically for high-lead logging, in use by Koster Products in 1926. This sled is in A-1 shape. Drums were narrow but deep. Steam jams were on main drum and two-speed unit. Notice the absence of leaking steam. Lee Johnson, the engineer, took pride in keeping the plumbing tight. Note the double-deck fairlead. The use of this type of fairlead was possible with the haulback drum on top of the mainline with both drums installed in line. Note also the offset house which had definite advantages in shielding the operator from the weather. Fireman Elbert Kelly is standing on the sled. *Lee Johnson photograph, author's collection*

In Search of Steam Donkeys

292

Another view of the 12 x 14 two-speed yarder bought by Nehalem Timber & Logging Co. of Scapoose, Oregon, previously shown on page 107. This photograph was taken in February of 1926. *W.I.S.Co. collection, courtesy of Jack Taylor.*

THE END OF AN ERA, 26 JUNE, 1957

Dilapidated sled runners and sheet metal were not un-usual on working donkeys. In this case, however, these were indications of impending doom for this Willamette Two-Speed yarder north of Keasey, Oregon. My father, Lee Johnson, was fortunate to be there the last day this yarder was used. Unfortunately, when Lee arrived, they were just pulling in the lines. Lee was about to approach Jack Easter, the yarder engineer, about the possibility of cracking open the throttle to hear it bark one more time, but Jack had other duties to attend to. Thus ended an era with little fanfare. It is sad to relate that this machine was scrapped on site. The loader at that "side" was also steam. Note the tree-rigged heel boom with railroad rails attached on edge to provide a better grip when heeling up logs.

The change to gas and diesel power was not readily ac-cepted by everyone in the logging industry. Later that year, Jack's next job was running a twin-engine diesel yarder for Diamond Lumber Company on the north fork of the Trask River, southeast of Tillamook, Oregon. I was a choker setter on that side the first day he arrived. True to the Easter tradi-tion (a family of loggers), he handled the job well. At the end of the day I asked him how he compared this yarder to the Willamette steamer. The answer came almost before I finished the question: "Hell, that Willamette would pull more in high gear than this will in low!"   *Photo by John T. Labbe*

THE LAST WILLAMETTE TWO-SPEED
YARDER TO OPERATE IN OREGON?

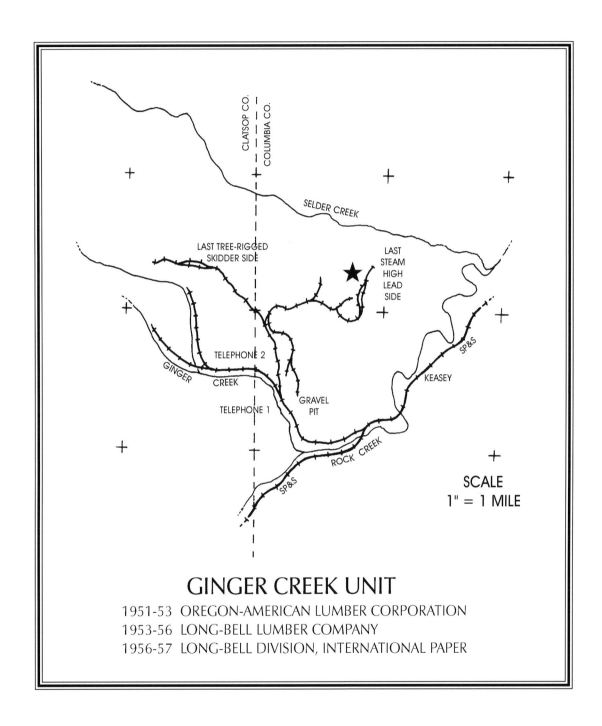

GINGER CREEK UNIT
1951-53 OREGON-AMERICAN LUMBER CORPORATION
1953-56 LONG-BELL LUMBER COMPANY
1956-57 LONG-BELL DIVISION, INTERNATIONAL PAPER

The star on the map shows the location of what may be the last Willamette Two-speed yarder used in Oregon. This operation was previously Oregon-American Lumber Co., of Vernonia. In 1957, it was International Paper Co., Long Bell Division, Vernonia Branch, Camp McGregor Division, Ginger Creek. The eventual shutdown of steam there was late summer or early fall, 1957. *Map courtesy of Jim Blain and Ed Kamholz as compiled by John Labbe and Don Devere.*

RARE PHOTOS!

These four photos show three donkeys at one tree, landing two turns of logs at once!

This tree had two skylines with Willamette two-speed yarders yarding at once, along with a loading donkey with a hay-rack boom. The yarding crews moved toward each other as the road changes were made.

In the photo at right, we are looking up at the tree with two skylines yarding at the same time. The hay-rack boom is visible near the bottom.

The bottom photo shows one of the Willamette two-speeds up close. Note the extended firebox. The spring pole and whistle wire drum bedeck the house. As was often the case, the houses tended to get battered, especially the extensions. These photos and information are courtesy of Felix Wilcoxen of Booth-Kelly at Camp Wendling, 1920. Felix was thirteen years old at the time and held the job of whistle punk there.

(Note: Yarding with more than one unit on any one spar tree was later outlawed.)

Above   There are three donkeys working at one tree in this landing at Booth-Kelly's Camp Wendling operation. The loading crew must have kept busy!

Below   Two turns of logs coming into the landing at the same time. The yarding crews moved toward each other as road changes were made.   *Photos by Felix Wilcoxen*

NOYES-HOLLAND ON THE KERRY LINE

A Noyes-Holland Logging Company crew pauses for the photographer. Noyes-Holland logged on the south side and above the famous tunnel of the Kerry Line (Columbia & Nehalem River RR) in the Coast Range of northwest Oregon. Noyes-Holland's railroad connected to this line. The Willamette direct-geared two-speed yarder (not a compound) shown here was built with a different size gear on each side of the main drum. Engaging the drum with either gear provided a choice of two speeds. Note the pipe which routed cinders down from the spark arrestor. *Photo courtesy of John Labbe.*

Both photographs on this page taken by Clark Kinsey at Deer Island Logging Co.   *Courtesy of John Labbe*

BENSON TIMBER COMPANY YARDING

This winter logging scene shows how tree-length logs look when they enter the landing. These long logs were destined to be made into the famous Benson "cigar" rafts that were used to move logs down the Pacific Coast to the Benson mill in San Diego, California. This yarder sports a round, steel water tank. *Clark Kinsey photograph from the Rudy Larson Collection*

In Search of Steam Donkeys

Can you figure out this system? There are several spar trees in this photo. The spar tree in the foreground appears to be a yarding tree, but with a homemade tree shoe about a third of the way from the top, used to support the "swing tree" skyline. If so, the "swing" system would take the logs to a crotch-line loading system.With Benson Timber Company's long logs, it is assumed that loading was done here with a crotch-line system. For those who take interest in such things, the yarder drops logs on the opposite side of their destination. In order for the "swing" crew to reach them, it was necessary to "tail-hold" beyond the yarder tree, which appears to be out of sight and to the left in this photo.   *Clark Kinsey photograph from Rudy Larson collection*

Compound Geared Yarders

REEDSPORT DONKEY MOVED OUT OF THE WOODS

In 1995, after 57 years of seclusion, Machine No. 36, a Smith & Watson Iron Works steam donkey near Reedsport, Oregon was moved to the Umpqua Discovery Center in town. After ten years of planning and scheming, Grover Woods has realized his dream of seeing the 12x13 yarder brought out of the woods. By 1994, he and his volunteer crew had it resting on a temporary sled built to assist in the move.

Grover ran all three donkeys owned by Winchester Bay Lumber Co. of Reedsport, Oregon, including this one. The operators did their own repairs on these machines. Loggers could plug a leaking flue during the working day and start logging again by pulling the fire and throwing timbers on the grates so they would have something to stand on which wouldn't burn their shoes. Yes, it was hot! The job of a donkey doctor was hard, just like all the jobs in a logging camp.

The Smith & Watson donkeys were noted for their steaming efficiency with their "square" fireboxes. This "convertible" gearing, as the factory listed them, provided two speeds

on the main drum. Gearing was changed when stopped. They were often referred to as "sledge-hammer two-speeds" by the loggers. Grover recalls some damage once done to one of the wings on the house, caused by a bull-block "dee" which broke and flew out of the tree.

According to Grover, this donkey was brought in from Portland on the Southern Pacific. His conversations with Bill Esselstrom, local old-timer, set the delivery date at 1915. Grover and others have determined that Machine No. 36 was originally put to work nearly two miles from its unloading spot. From there it was moved from spar to spar, clearing timber from Reedsport to Winchester Bay, and eventually headed up Winchester Creek, logging spurs as the railroad was built.

The logging railroad started at the log dump at Winchester (now the site of the Coast Guard station). As the railroad reached the woods, it continued along on the bottom of the nearby canyons. When the railroad was built, piling was driven to bridge the swamps in the area. The piling has long

In Search of Steam Donkeys

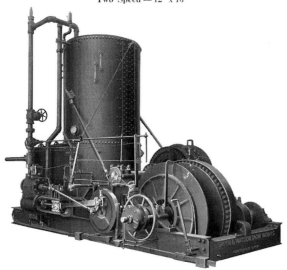

"S. & W." Compound Geared "Universal" Yarder
Two Speed — 12" x 13"

Above Factory illustration from undated Smith & Watson catalog. *Author's collection*

Opposite Machine No. 36 at Winchester, Oregon, 1935. Left to right: Jack Carlson, rigging slinger; Rex Carlson, whistle punk; Pete Knight, choker-setter; Floyd Hoyt, camp foreman; Carl Carlson, engineer; Percy Dickerson, climber; Lee Speares, wood buck; Archie Kennedy, chaser; the last man was Carmel. *Clark Kinsey photo, Grover Woods collection*

Below right The Smith & Watson yarder awaiting its move up the mountain on a temporary sled built by Grover Woods. Mike Waggoner, upper, Grover, lower. *Photo by the author*

OWNER Location Builder Type Bore & Stroke	Umpquah Discovery Center Reedsport, Oregon Smith & Watson Compound Geared Convertible Yarder 12 x 13				Machine #36
	D	**W**	**L**	**THICK**	**H**
FRAME SIZE		96	238	6-1/4	15
PIN. GEAR, LOW	14	7-1/2			
PIN. GEAR, HI	16	6-1/2			
MAIN PINION	12	7-1/5			
INTERM. GEAR	35	4			
CRANK DISC	30	3-1/2			
FIREBOX		68	110		70
BOILER	68				156
SMOKEBOX	67				47

	FLANGE DIA	CORE D/W	GEAR & BRAKE PD	F/ WIDTH	SHAFT DIA
MAIN DRUM	66	28/17	72	7	6-7/8
MAIN BRAKE	65			5	
H/B DRUM	52	20/18	42-1/2	8	4-3/4
H/B BRAKE	41			4-3/4	6-1/4
STRAW DRUM	26-1/2	11/14.5	12-1/2	4-1/2	3-7/8
STRAW BRAKE	19			4-1/2	3-7/8
GYPSY	18/16	11.5/15	35	4	6-1/2

Additional data:
  69 ft. original sled   1-3/8 mainline cable   408 2" flues
  3" steam supply pipe   6 ft. x 117" tank

since rotted away, with little evidence remaining today. Grover recalls them driving piling full length into the swamp bottom, then sometimes having to drive another piling on top until they stopped being swallowed up in the mud. Machine No. 36 logged its way through solid timber, (mostly spruce, some fir) from the Reedsport depot to its last landing. The yarding in the Winchester Creek Canyon was done from the top of the ridges. The logs were then skylined ("swung") down hill by this yarder placed near the railroad at the bottom.

In the 1990s, with the donkey still at the bottom of the canyon and the piling long since rotted away, access was difficult. There was no way to haul it out of that swamp from the bottom. It remained there from 1937 until Grover managed to put a little life into the situation. The Smith & Watson yarder couldn't be taken out from below, but neither could it be moved directly up the hill from its hiding place. (The huge yarder in its day weighed from 27 to 37 tons with rigging.) With considerable planning, it was decided to build a half-mile cat road along the edge of the swamp at the bottom of the hillside. Thanks to Waggoner & Murphy Logging Company and others, the road was built. This enabled them to get it to a place where they could yard it uphill. The next leg of the journey was uphill 1,000 feet at

Compound Geared Yarders

Machine No. 36

Left   The fuel/water tank in the background is ready to be moved. The yarder is close to its ascent up the hill. *Photo by the author*

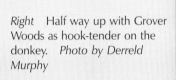

Right   Half way up with Grover Woods as hook-tender on the donkey.   *Photo by Derreld Murphy*

Left   Bruce Gerard's truck-mounted tower and two crawler tractors. The front of the truck occasionally lifted up when pulling. Not visible in the photo is the chasm below with the front wheels of the truck on the edge of the canyon. *Photo by Darreld Murphy*

shut down early one day, and later supplied a low boy for the haul into town. The machine that did the bulk of the work was a small homemade truck mounted tower owned by Bruce Gerard. Three crawler tractors, the tower (with leverage supplied by two to three blocks on the yarder sled), and additional blocks on the side-hill and at the landing, proved once again that loggers can do it! It was a slow process which inched the old girl up the hill. It was also a labor intensive process. There was much speculation on methods of rigging and how to minimize pulling strawline by hand, but Grover hadn't forgotten his rigging skills, and things went as planned.

Grover had his hands full with planning, rigging, organizing equipment and labor, but he made it happen, all gratis. The August event was attended by many of the townsfolk, with cameras, video cameras, binoculars, and kids, who viewed the spectacle from the landing on top of the ridge.

45 degrees. It was necessary to hook on to the boiler and side-block to keep it from tipping over.

The ridge top is now a winding truck road. One of the landings on that ridge was the site where the steamer was to be loaded onto the low boy that day in August of 1994. International Paper had a side with a tower about a hundred feet away from the landing from the proposed site. They

A new "sled" for this machine is in the works. With fabricated ribs covered with painted and textured concrete similar to boat construction, the sled will be made to look like logs, but should last forever.

Above and below Near the end of a hard pull. Note the rigging and machines needed to do this. *Photos by Derreld Murphy*

RIGGER'S NIGHTMARE

Care to figure this one out? Perhaps the early donkey in the background just didn't have enough power to pull the machine in the foreground without the leverage of 12 blocks! The sled being dragged appears to have rails, implying that the load may be a locomotive being salvaged or moved to isolated trackage, such as the top of an incline. It looks as though a lot of cable was spooled on the drum for each small gain of that day. These photos, by Ed Stamm, of unknown date are of Pacific Lumber Co. of Scotia, California. When steam donkeys needed to be moved under their own power, one moving block was yarded out to a stump with the mainline in it and the eye tail holded into the sled plate. This is a very rare photograph.   *John Labbe collection.*

According to Bridal Veil Lumber Company records, this was the very first sky-line. Bill Dyche built this carriage in 1899. Although the sophisticated skyline systems did not come into general use until years later, this was an innovative beginning for the development of logging methods in the Pacific Northwest. Not much else is known about this, but one would be led to speculate as to whether it is a gravity return or "shotgun" feed, since only one cable that connects to the carriage is visible. Note the "farmer's eye" in the skidding line which is also connected above the swivel by means of a "Molly Hogan." Note also the use of "swamp hooks" or "logging dogs" to hold the logs. *John Labbe collection*

Compound Geared Yarders

In Search of Steam Donkeys

CHAPTER 4

LOADERS

As the methods of yarding changed from ground lead to high-lead, it was a natural sequence of events to get the rigging into the air to load logs as well.

In the early days, a small donkey was used to parbuckle* logs to railroad cars from a rollway. Later, loading systems were developed that became as complicated as yarding systems, in many cases, much more so. It was common to yard and load with the same spar tree, which resulted in a myriad of lines, shackles and blocks.

Loaders were sometimes mounted with the yarder. The combined yarder-loaders (some with steel towers) were called "units." Almost all of these machines were "unit skidders," and railcar-mounted. Unfortunately, all of those used in Oregon were scrapped, but they were significant to Oregon logging history. First used in the South as high-lead machines, they were the forerunners of the giant machines that were developed to handle Pacific Northwest timber. Aside from two "units" on display in Washington State, and the remote possibility that a 16 by 73 foot machine with a 100-foot tower could be hiding somewhere in the brush, Oregon and the rest of the Northwest have lost out.

Loading methods included heel booms, hayrack booms, crotch lines, gin poles, and guyline (also called jackline) systems. Some of these systems are shown in this chapter.

This chapter deals with loaders other than McGifferts. Some small yarders were used as loaders, but the Willamette loaders on these pages were built specifically as loaders and were commonly used on tree-rigged booms and crotch line systems.

Left   Clark Kinsey captured the essence of Northwest steam logging in this view of a Smith-Powers Logging Company landing.   *Martin E. Hansen Collection*

---

*   The use of a cable passed under and back over a log, causing it to roll when the cable is pulled.

WILLAMETTE IRON AND STEEL WORKS

LOADING ENGINES

Standard Three-Drum Loading Engine

This type of loader has been in general use for a number of years, and is recognized as a standard loading engine.

The 9¼ x 10 or the 10 x 11 loading engines are conceded to be the proper size for the satisfactory handling of the heavy West Coast timber. All Willamette features of the yarding engines such as cut steel gearing, monkey motion valve gear, high pressure boiler, etc., are embodied in this type of equipment.

All drums are controlled from operator's side.

WILLAMETTE IRON AND STEEL WORKS

LOADING ENGINES

Loading Engine Department.

Some operators have found it advisable, owing to the lead of loading lines to the tree, to reverse the drum arrangement and place the narrow drums in back and the wide drum in front, as shown. This can be done at the purchaser's option, and in no way affects the operating efficiency of the engine.

Complete specifications of either size loader with the drum arrangement desired will be furnished on request.

The loaders depicted above are two versions showing the various drum arrangements available from Willamette Iron & Steel Works. As many as five drums could be ordered on Willamette loaders. One use for the extra drums was to yard in firewood logs and other "chunking out chores." On machine No. 37, both mainline and haulback are on the same shaft. The drum speeds (and there-fore, power) were determined by the drum's core diameter. The main drum on this one would be upper right because it has a small core, and the haulback would be upper left (large core). The car drum (lower) is identified by the ratchet and pawl construction to hold cars as they are loaded. *1925 W.I.S.Co. catalog, pp. 52 and 53, Glen Comstock Collection.*

SLACK-LINE LOGGING WITH A HEEL BOOM IN THE SPAR TREE

This drawing depicts an elaborate system of high-lead logging during the heyday of steam. The slack-line system required one more drum than required by the basic high-lead yarding system. "Slackers" were equipped with a minimum of three yarding drums plus a strawline drum. Two sets of guylines were needed for the slacker yarding system. In addition, four buckle guys were needed to support the loading system. In the example shown, a total of 14 guys are used (not all visible in this sketch). "Disconnect" log cars, donkeys equipped with "houses" (roofs), and spark arrestors, were a common sight during this era.

In all probability, the yarder shown would have been equipped with air controls. Some also had additional equipment, such as two-speed gearing on the skidding line drum.

There are some minor errors which loggers of the era might detect. Can you find them? *Drawn by the author, 1992*

Willamette high lead loader, crotch line rigged, using straps.   *Sketch by Lynn M. Sabol*

CLATSKANIE, OREGON,

Above The Benson Timber Company letterhead, showing their famous long log loads and disconnect logcars with link and pin couplers. Benson used these long logs in their ocean-going "cigar" log rafts. *Courtesy of Ed Danielson*

Below Crotch-line loading. One of many methods of rigging a crotch-line loading system. A favorite alternate is to use a skyline and anchor the mainline into the carriage as it comes out of the fall block. *Author's drawing, 1995*

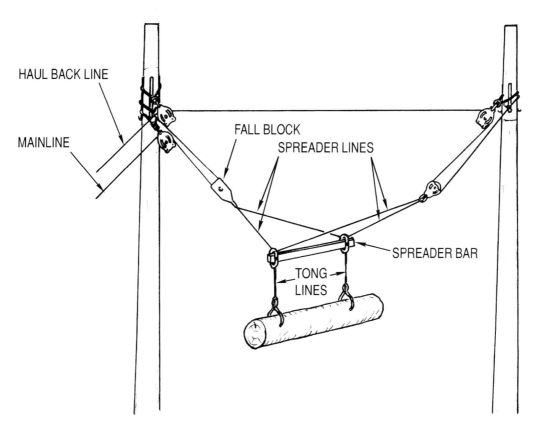

HAUL BACK LINE

MAINLINE

FALL BLOCK

SPREADER LINES

SPREADER BAR

TONG LINES

MACHINE NO. 37

Willamette Iron & Steel Works records show Machine No. 37 was shipped new to Pacific Spruce Corp. at Toledo, Oregon in 1922. It was later owned by C.D. Johnson Lumber. Co., and then Georgia-Pacific Corp. (both in Toledo). In 1958 it was donated to the Pioneer Logging Museum in Portland, Oregon. This was the original Forestry Building built in 1905 for the Lewis & Clark Exhibition, with logs supplied by Simon Benson. The loader remained at the Forestry Building until it burned in 1964, after which it was moved to Delta Park in Portland. From Delta Park, it and its companion, a Dolbeer donkey (machine No. 1) were moved onto a privately owned machine shop yard in Milwaukie, Oregon. The next move was in the 1980s, to its present location at Camp 18 Logging Museum near Elsie, Oregon.

Above Machine No. 37 on display at its present location, Camp 18 Logging Museum near Elsie, Oregon. *Author's photo*

Above Machine No. 37 at Delta Park in the early 70s. *Lee Johnson photo*

OWNER	Camp 18 Logging Museum				Machine #37
Location	Elsie, Oregon				
Builder	Willamette Iron & Steel Works S/N 1790				
Type	Loader				
Bore & Stroke	11 x 13				
	D	W	L	THICK	H
FRAME SIZE		74-1/2	174	6	15
PINION GEAR	10	7-1/2			
CRANK DISC	30	3-3/4			
BOILER	54				125
SMOKEBOX	49				

	FLANGE DIA	CORE D/W	GEAR & BRAKE PD	F/ WIDTH	SHAFT DIA
MAIN DRUM	33/53	18/16	58	6	5-1/2
MAIN BRAKE	53			2-1/4	
H/B DRUM	55-1/2	40/15.5	58	5	5-1/2
H/B BRAKE	55-1/2			4	
CAR DRUM	34	14.5/14	41	6	5-1/2
CAR BRAKE	34			6	

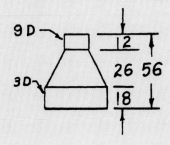

Additional data:
Pinion shaft: 4-3/4

Willamette valve gear up close. Machine No. 37. *Photos by the author, 1983*

Left Machine No. 37 at the Portland Forestry Building on Vaughn Street before it burned. *John Cummings*

NOTES ON THE CAR DRUM

Loaders such as Machine No. 37 were equipped with a main drum for lifting the log; a haulback drum for returning the rigging or boom; and a car drum to move railroad cars as they were loaded. The car drum was mounted on the right front of the donkey (lower shaft). (The operator's position is on the right side as he faces forward.) The car drum is equipped with a steam brake and dog. The friction mechanism is on the left end of the drum shaft, but with controls on the right. Since the fireman would often control the car drum, it would seem logical that the mechanism be installed on the left, but the deciding factor appears to be the lack of space on the right when these donkeys were equipped with quadrant controls. These controls were installed alongside the car drum to provide an alternate method of controlling the donkey. Quadrant controls were also used on incline machines, and were offered as an option on this type of hoist.

Below left and right Machine No. 37 in a shop in Milwaukie, Oregon, 1978. *Author's photo*

A 10 x 11 Willamette loader, brand-new on November 14, 1923, before shipment to Nehalem Timber & Logging Co. of Scapoose, Oregon. Nearly identical to Machine No. 38 (now at Camp 18), it is listed as model No. MLSCR-D39. Note the chain and sprockets on the left side, which enabled the operator to control the friction on the car drum. On these loaders not equipped with a chain-driven remote control, the fireman operated the car drum. *Photo courtesy Oregon Historical Society, W.I.S.Co. collection photo No. 2573*

MACHINE No. 38

MOVING DAY, 1978

Machine No. 38 had its beginnings in August, 1922 with Beaver Creek Logging Company, near Beaver Creek, Oregon. The selling price was $5,900. The Willamette records list this machine as "MLSCR class D39." The same records show it in the possession of Connacher Logging Company at Glenwood, Oregon, with no date. (Connacher was in Glenwood from approximately 1935 to 1942.)

According to a local publication, Booth-Kelly Lumber Co. of Wendling, Oregon had it in 1948, and then Row River Lumber Co. used it at a reload from the log pond on the O.P.&E. Rwy. at Springfield, Oregon, loading peeler logs for Springfield Plywood until early 1959.

It eventually came into the possession of Georgia Pacific Corp., who donated it to the Lane County Museum in Eugene, Oregon. It was put on display in the front of the museum in 1978. Les Calder spearheaded this movement. Western Machinery Company donated a sled from an internal combustion donkey. The Jay Oldham Co. provided the equipment and labor to move it from the rear of the museum to its display location in front and place it on the sled.

This machine was recently moved to Camp 18 Logging Museum at Elsie, Oregon , and is now on display there.

Additional data:
  3" supply pipe to throttle valve,
  reduced before going to cylinders.
  12 x 16 firebox opening
  200 lb. working pressure

OWNER Location Builder Type Bore & Stroke	Camp 18 Logging Museum Elsie, Oregon Willamette Iron & Steel Works S/N 2077 Loader 10 x 11				Machine #38
	D	W	L	THICK	H
FRAME SIZE		74-1/2	148/154.5	5-1/2	15
PINION GEARS	7-1/2	5			
CRANK DISC	26	3			
BOILER	54				125
SMOKEBOX	49				44
	FLANGE DIA	CORE D/W	GEAR & BRAKE PD	F/ WIDTH	SHAFT DIA
MAIN DRUM	40	12/38.5	41	5	4-1/2
MAIN BRAKE	38			4	
H/B DRUM	33	18/17	42	5	5-1/2
H/B BRAKE	32-1/2			4	
CAR DRUM	34	18/16	42	5	5-1/2
CAR BRAKE	33-1/2			2	

In Search of Steam Donkeys

Opposite top   Machine No. 38 on the low-boy moving trailer at the Lane County Museum in Eugene, Oregon.

Opposite bottom   The sled came from an internal combustion donkey. Here the sled is being placed into position for display with Machine No. 38.

Right   Lowering Machine No. 38 onto its new sled at the Lane County Museum.

Below   Machine No. 38 on display at the museum.

Photos by Bill Hudson, 1978

Above   A tree-rigged loading boom. There are no tree jacks visible. The two sail guys appear to be tail-held into the tree. The upper sail guy appears to be spliced near the tree, and the loading line has a high lead block hanging from a sail guy line. Note also the proportionate height of the top sail guy where it approaches the tree relative to the length of the boom. These methods are controversial.   *Weister photo, location or date unknown, from Amel/Meyer collection*

Opposite   The same unidentified setting, with a log swung over the track ready for loading. Note the small diameter of the boom sticks.   *Weister photo from John T. Labbe Collection*

Loaders

In Search of Steam Donkeys

Above   Machine No. 39   Author's photo, 1977

Machine No. 39 is preserved in a locked shop, complete with blocks and rigging. With all of these pieces intact, there is the potential to recreate an entire system! The donkey rests on a dolly that steers.

Brookings Commercial purchased it new on January 13, 1918 as engine No. 1525 type EHB, class Q-10. Other Willamette records list it as "MLSCJ D-4" delivered on April 15, 1918. Kimball Brothers Lumber Company used it at a mill cold deck rigged to a crotch line with skyline. Jim Hubbard purchased it in 1960. It is now owned by N.B. Giustina.

Note the wood lagging used as a brake lining substitute. This was sometimes used where slippage was minimal, especially in loading, as opposed to high lead shows. It was not uncommon to see tree-rigged boom loaders minus the main drum brake altogether because the log could be held up with the throttle open and the friction on. Lowering was accomplished by easing up on the throttle and allowing the engines to run backwards or slipping the friction.

Opposite   Crotch-line loading with tongs. Unidentified. Weister photo, Oregon Historical Society, W.I.S.Co. Collection, No. OrHi 92955

OWNER	N.B. (Nat) Giustina				Machine
Location	private display				#39
Builder	Willamette Iron & Steel Works S/N 1525				
Type	Loader				
Bore & Stroke	9-1/4 x 10				
	D	W	L	THICK	H
FRAME SIZE		66	150	5-1/2	15
PINION GEARS	7-1/2 8-1/2	5			
CRANK DISC	22	3			
BOILER	48				108
	FLANGE DIA	CORE D/W	GEAR & BRAKE PD F/ WIDTH		SHAFT DIA
MAIN DRUM	40	/30	41	4-1/2	
MAIN BRAKE				4	
H/B DRUM	34	/12	43		
CAR DRUM	34	/12	43		

CROTCH-LINE LOADING

Landing logs on a crotch-line deck. Notice the North Bend yarding system and the use of "plain" end hooks on the spreader bar. End hooks without bells (cups) were later outlawed. *Weister photo, location and date unknown, from Amel/Meyer collection*

In Search of Steam Donkeys

TWO MORE CROTCH-LINE SYSTEMS IN ACTION

Above   Unidentified crotch-line loading scene, from L.P. Kremer collection

Below   Loading long logs at Deer Island Logging Company.   *Clark Kinsey photo, John Labbe collection.*

Above As crotch-line systems evolved, the use of tongs became common. Oregon-American Lumber Company used this system as a reload from trucks to the railroad.

Below Heel boom loading at a landing in the woods. Heel booms used one tong and were lined on the underside with railroad iron to facilitate "heeling" up one end of the log. This photo was taken at Camp Olsen, 1955. Both photos are of Long-Bell Lumber Company, out of Vernonia, Oregon. This company was originally Oregon-American. *Both photos courtesy of Alvin Elkins*

In Search of Steam Donkeys

This is another photo of Long-Bell Lumber Company's operation of the former Oregon-American Lumber Co., taken at the "last skidder side" at Ginger Creek, shown on the map on page 115, circa 1956. This was the last tree-rigged skidder used there. They had two skidders in operation there, a tower skidder and a tree-rigged skidder. This side used a tree-rigged skidder. The disconnect trucks were loaded with the tree-rigged heel boom shown. Note the position of the block and strap rigged to swing the boom to the left. Normally the "squirrel chunk" pulled the boom over the car to be loaded. The squirrel chunk was a small, unmerchantable log used as a counterweight to pull the boom in one direction. It is out of sight in the photo. Note also the neat row of bolts with bridge washers holding the boom together.   *Ralph Swan photo*

CROTCH-LINE LOADING, BENSON TIMBER CO.

How many spar trees can you count? This view shows yarding or swinging logs via the North Bend system to a crotch-line loading system. This is another Benson Timber Co. operation near Benson Lookout Road. The timber in the background belonged to Clark & Wilson Lumber Co. Rudy Larson remembers this landing quite vividly due to an accident he had following a forest fire there. A lot of bark typically collects around landings like this. Rudy once stepped right through a seemingly innocuous bark pile which was still a bed of hot coals underneath! Spar trees occasionally broke under the strains of yarding and loading. Although it did not happen here, Benson Timber Company once broke one below the high lead block, dropping the rigging in a pile, at South Fork out of Swede Town, Oregon. *Notes and C. Kinsey photograph courtesy Rudy Larson.*

In Search of Steam Donkeys

Above More crotch-line loading at Benson Timber Company out of Clatskanie, Oregon. Note use of link and pin couplers on the disconnects. Benson preferred these old-style couplers and never changed. They were probably one of the last of the western loggers to use them.

Below This view illustrates Benson's policy of yarding tree-length logs to the landing and loading them with a crotch-line. *Both photos by C. Kinsey, from Rudy Larson collection*

Above Heel boom loading, Connacher Logging Co. at Glenwood, Oregon, 1942. *C. Kinsey photograph, author's collection*

HEEL BOOM LOADING

The drawing on the next page shows the loading portion of a spar tree. It is important to note that this is a simplified schematic of the rigging. The drawing is not to scale. In most cases, the tree would be much taller than portrayed, with the upper portion (not shown) used for yarding, and containing six or more guylines. For a complete rigging system, see page 131.

Numbered items in drawing:

1. **Guylines** - If this spar tree is used for loading and yarding, these "buckle guys" are the lower set of guys which support the loading system. If so, four are required.

2. **Sail guy** - Holds the front end of the boom up.

3. **Guyline carriage** - Two blocks can be used instead.

4. **Tree shoe** - It is best not to use a block for this. A standing line (a line that is not regularly in motion via a drum) can

crystallize near the block sheave. This happened to a skyline that broke at Consolidated Timber Co. Following that incident, their crews needed no persuasion to use a tree shoe. The shoes are built with edge-grain hardwood lining in the bottom.

5. **Mainline to loading donkey**

6. **Bullblock for the mainline**

7. **Haulback to loading donkey**

8. **Tong line**

9. **Squirrel line** - Used to return the boom. Not shown is a common practice of threading this line through a block in the tree.

10. **Squirrel "chunk"** - Usually a piece of wood approximately four feet in diameter and 8 to 10 feet long. The weight of the squirrel chunk returns the boom. These

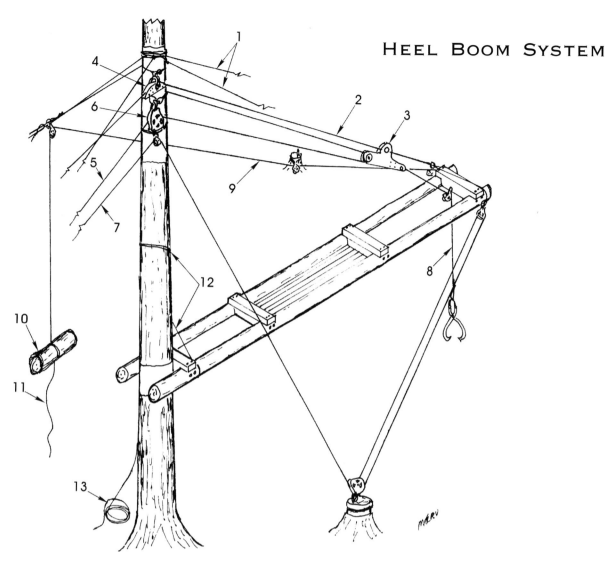

can be hung in various places and in various ways. Some loggers preferred to hang them from another tree.

11. Tag line - A safety device used to warn a logger, if he was standing under the squirrel chunk. Later, the Industrial Accident Commission required a fence around the tag line.

12. Heel strap - This was a quarter-twist to assist the squirrel (gravity) in returning the boom. Not shown also, are two straps about five or six feet long going around the boom sticks, which connect to a strap or choker which in turn, is hung in the tree as shown. The heel strap is a three-piece arrangement. The boom is powered toward the deck, and gravity pulls it over the load.

13. Not shown is where the squirrel line goes after entering the block on the front of the boom. A rigging chain is attached to the cable, and it is pulled along the boom stick toward the tree until the squirrel chunk is at the correct height from the ground. At that point, it is half-hitched several times around one of the boom sticks near the tree (where it won't rub). The remainder is coiled into a pile. This is how the take up is adjusted when rigging up.

Unlike the hayrack boom, which used two tongs, a heel boom uses only one tong with steel rails attached on edge underneath to heel up the log. Their forerunners were the manufactured heel-booms on Lidgerwood steel spar tower skidders, used long before a counterpart came into common use on a spar tree. The date of the origin of the heel boom is in dispute. Photographic evidence shows heel booms in use as early as 1929. Interviews that I have held with retired loggers seem to indicate the time of their popularity as much later than that. When they first rigged one at Consolidated Timber Company in 1937, some top brass from other outfits came to visit. Heel booms, along with their counterpart, the hayrack boom, slowly faded with the demise of the wooden spar tree. In this author's experience in Tillamook County, there were few (if any) tree-rigged booms still in use by 1957 due to the advent of the mobile loaders. The wooden spar tree persisted much longer (without booms), although few were used. I don't know how long Simpson Timber Co. continued to use one or two wooden trees, but they were still there into the mid-1970s.

Shown on Page 252 is an illustration of a heel boom designed by Young Iron Works. This is probably the ultimate in heel booms, with the chafing plates and steel plates for hanging. Most booms were not so elaborate. Lengths of booms could vary considerably. Consolidated Timber Co. of

Above A Willamette three-drum loader owned by Clark & Wilson Lumber Company. With its double-extended firebox and piston valves, this is a fairly modern machine, even though it's a wood-burner. Also, note the chunks of metal roofing placed at the wing to roof joint to protect the operator from rain drips. *Clark Kinsey photo from Martin E. Hansen Collection*

Glenwood, Oregon used long heel-booms, probably because a lot of their logs were 64 feet long or longer. A long boom would provide more options as to where a deck could be built (logs waiting to being loaded). Some long booms sagged with the small boom sticks, but no one seemed to mind. It was possible to break heel-booms. I recall a case where the yarder engineer accidentally dropped a log onto the boom.

Some heel-booms were tapered (wider at the tree.) This was not necessary, and did tend to limit heeling options a little. If, on the other hand, the heel-boom was designed to straddle a seven foot diameter tree there would be a lot of wood in it if there were no taper. It was better to hang them horizontally. If the heel was lower, the logs tended to shift forward as they were placed on the load. As to height, some loggers hung heel booms 20 to 22 feet from the ground. Using the same height every time simplified the rig-up pro-

cess. We are talking about a time much different from today, however, when they knew ahead of time the average lengths of logs and where the next settings would be. These factors determined the height and length of boom.

Thanks to these loggers for their expertise: Archie Saling (via Lionel Youst), Archie Samuel, Howard Clark, Chet Anderson, Bert Pickens, Howard Stratton, and Lee Johnson. Unfortunately, most of these guys have gone on to the "hook-tender in the sky," but their memory and expertise live on!

Heel-Boom Dimensions

Approximate sizes: Main line = 1-1/4"; haulback= 7/8"; most blocks = 14"; tie rod bolt size = 1" or 1-1/4".

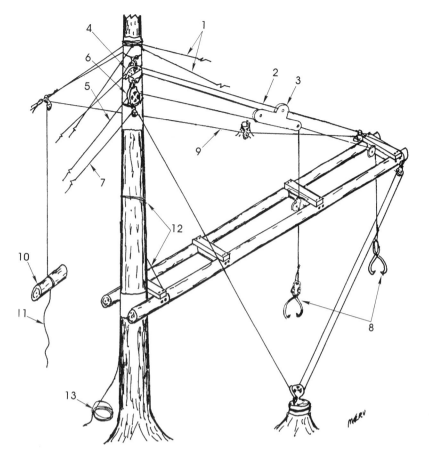

HAYRACK BOOM SYSTEM

Left: The hayrack boom system is basically identical to the heel boom system except that two tongs are used instead of one. The item numbers correspond to the heel boom system previously shown. *Author's drawing*

Below A setting of Western Lumber Company of Westfir, Oregon, loading with a hayrack boom. The log to the right of the boom is being brought in by the yarder in the background. *John T. Labbe Collection*

Loaders

SURVIVAL AND SUCCESS
C.E. (VAN) VAN CISE

The steam logging era provided an avenue for financial survival and, on occasion high wages, for many. The loggers came from all walks of life. Many were immigrants, some lived near logging communities, others came from the farms, where it was difficult to make a living.

Higher education was not a criteria for being hired by a logging company. As a result, uneducated men who were willing to work and progress in their trade often did well. Some were of high intelligence who did not have the means to attend school. C.E. (Van) Van Cise (1900-1971) is a case in point. He came to the West from a small Wisconsin farm community. As a boy in Wisconsin, he and his family experienced a rigorous life. Work had a higher priority than schooling. Completing the fifth grade was the extent of his formal education. He later became self-educated, however, through study and reading what he could (for example, classic literature and as a subscriber to *Atlantic Monthly* and *Harpers*). His job as head of construction for Crown Zellerbach sometimes required him to solve engineering problems. Prior to his assignment at Tillamook, he was asked to be superintendent (woods boss). Even though he declined the offer, this must have been quite a personal triumph.

While Van had no ambition to get his memoirs into print, it is fortunate that the family saved them in his longhand rough draft form. The memoirs have at last surfaced, in spite of the barely visible pencil compositions on half-torn note-

book paper. Here is the first paragraph of what remains of his autobiography:

> As a boy, I lived with my parents and two brothers in a rather backward area in Southern Wisconsin. Half of the farms were abandoned and reverted to the county for nonpayment of taxes; the buildings run down and the fields grown over with young jack pines. In the seven years we lived there we lived on five farms and never paid a cent in rent. No one expected it. Two of the places belonged to a man living about fifty miles away, (a hard two days journey each way with horse and buggy over those sandy roads) and he was glad to have someone there just to keep the buildings in repair and prevent the neighbors from running off with the doors and windows. The whereabouts of the owners of the other three places we occupied at different times was unknown. They were just gone, that was all. My father was a blacksmith and followed his trade from one construction project to another, and was at home only between jobs. We survived as best we could on the land, and always had a big garden and plenty of chores to keep us busy......

The next four stories are recollections Van had of working

Left A gin-pole loading scene from about 1913. "Billdad" Howell was a contractor for Sturtevant & Craine of Coquille, Oregon, who logged for Prosper Mill Company. This view was taken near Sevenmile Creek (or slough?), so named because it flows into the Coquille River seven miles from its mouth at Bandon, Oregon. The Sturtevant & Craine logging railroad consisted of three miles of 36" gauge track, two rod locomotives, ten log cars and a flatcar. Output was 50M per day. Shown in photo: Allen Leneve and Elmer McQue on log, Harry Hunt by loco, Jess Nelson sitting on spool of Dolbeer donkey.
Jack's Photo Service from John T. Labbe

Above   Crotch line loading at Coos Bay Lumber Company. The 8-spot, a 75-ton Heisler switches the cars. This engine (c/n 1349) was built new for Smith-Powers Logging Company in 1916. She then became Coos Bay Lumber Co.'s No. 8. She went on to work for Bradley Woodard Lumber Co., J.H. Chambers & Son, and finally, Lorane Valley Lumber Co. She always carried the number "8".   *Clark Kinsey photo, Martin E. Hansen Collection*

for Crown Zellerbach in Washington. Note his more-than-adequate command of the English language. The only editorial changes are the use of fictitious names. Rather remarkable for one who never had schooling beyond the fifth grade!

Carnival Harry

Carnival Harry made the rounds of the logging camps peddling jackknives, straightedge razors, secondhand jewelry, and pornography. His knives wouldn't cut, razors shave, nor watches keep time, but his pinups decorated bunkhouse walls all over the Northwest. He was a queer old coot who used to get into heated arguments with himself unmindful of bystanders. One sunny Sunday several of us young fellows were setting on a bridge railing fishing, when Harry hove into view with his pack of merchandise on his back. He was gesticulating excitedly and talking a blue streak. As he passed without looking up, we heard him say, "And Fred said to her, 'Turn over you old bitch.'" He slapped his thigh and went on up the hill laughing to himself, unaware that we even existed.

Joe the Bucker

Joe worked for Crown Zellerbach many years. He was a windfall bucker working alone with no one to talk with all day long. Being a loquacious old bird, he often talked to his own tools. If a twister had flattened all the timber in an area

and the trees were crisscross in a bucker's jackpot, he would discuss the lay with his saw, hammer, axe, and wedges before tackling the dangerous job of breaking it down; which tree to stand on, where to stand to be clear of kickbacks, and a hundred other things a man must learn if he is to survive the hazards of windfall bucking. He called one wedge "George" and the other "Harry," his axe "Mike," and sledge "Roscoe." One day as I made my rounds of the cutting crew, I came unseen upon Joe. He reached back and picked up his sledge and said apologetically, "Now Harry, I hate to do this, but I just got to give you another tap."

The Talking Watchman

In the days of steam logging, a watchman always fired up the skidder boilers about 5:00 A.M. so they would have a head of steam when the crew got there to start work at eight. We had a boxcar that we moved from time to time as the logging advanced along the railroad. One end was partitioned off for the scaler's office. The other end was the watchman's quarters. The car was located about 12 miles from camp one Fall when deer season opened. Spike and I had spotted a buck in that locality, so one Friday we took our rifles, a couple blankets and extra food, and placed them in the scaler's end of the boxcar. That evening instead of returning to camp, we

In Search of Steam Donkeys

stayed in the car overnight to get an early start hunting next morning. We made ourselves comfortable in the office, and were munching on some sandwiches that evening when the watchman returned after checking the water and fuel oil supply. Unaware of our presence, he opened the door to his end of the car and we heard him say to the empty room, "Hello there old lady, how the hell are you? What are we having for supper?"

Louis' New Breed of Chipmunks

The first summer I worked for Crown was hot and dry, and just before the Fourth of July shutdown the receding line on the Lidgerwood skidder siwashing a dead snag started a fire. It spread so rapidly there was no chance to control it. The best the crew could do was to drop the tower, cut the rigging loose, and move the skidder out, leaving the skyline, guys, walking anchors, blocks, and bicycle (carriage) to be destroyed by the intense heat. The mainline encircled the setting on three sides, and if we could keep the fire from jumping it, we had it made. So we wasted no time on trying to save the four million board feet of fell and bucked timber in the path of the raging inferno, but concentrated on stopping it at the railroad track. The engineer crew, of which I was a member, was given the job of keeping the construction camp watered down while our four timber fallers patrolled the siding where the office and the cook car stood. As the fire advanced, it drove a horde of squirrels and chipmunks ahead of the flames. By the time they reached the track, many of the poor little fellows were so exhausted they were barely able to creep across. With a perverted sense of humor, part of the crew seemed to get a sadistic satisfaction in nipping the tails off the helpless little creatures with their razor sharp axes.

Ten years had passed and I had forgotten the matter. At the time, we had been much too busy saving the construction camp to pay much attention to what was happening to the chipmunks. In the meantime, I had been transferred to Neah Bay. As I stepped off the mulligan upon returning from work one evening, who should I see but Louis Albin standing on the office porch. Louis was a jewelry salesman from Astoria and for more than twenty years had been making the rounds of the logging camps on the Columbia. The boys were always glad to see him, whether or not they were interested in his ware, as he was a pleasant, outgoing man, with the news and gossip of other camps and a source of new stories. After the customary greetings, he invited me to come over to the bunkhouse where he was spending the night. A bunch of his old friends were having a get-together after supper. By the time I got there, every bed and powder box in the room was preempted, so Louis moved over and motioned me to sit on the bunk next to him. The talk got around to Cathlamet and he turned to me and said, "Van, do you remember when they were moving the Willamette skidder and the grade gave way and it tipped over on its smokestack? Well I wanted to get a look at it, so I rode up on the speeder and stayed overnight at construction camp. Next morning on my way to the wreck, I passed the garbage dump and it was covered with chipmunks; at least half of them bobtailed as rabbits. I've talked with men all up and down the river and not one had ever heard of such a thing. Must be a new species developed in that area. Did you ever see any of them?"

Then it all came back to me. I remembered the men on fire patrol. Louis laughed hardest of all when he learned that it was man, not evolution, that had eliminated the chipmunks' tails. But I think he was a little disappointed I had spoiled a good theory.

Duplex Loaders

by Philip Schnell

The two Willamette catalog pages shown below illustrate the concept of duplex loading (also called "guyline" loading). This advanced and efficient loading system required a special engine equipped with two independent and reversible drums, one above the other, each powered by its own set of engines. The upper cylinder and crank disk can be seen in the catalog page below. Each drum was rigidly locked to its own shaft, so that direction of rotation could be instantly reversed with directional-control steam valves connected to the control levers.

Duplex loading was a two-tong system. The loading jacks and blocks were hung from guylines so that a suspended log would hang directly over a spotted rail car. When loading, the tongs were carried out and attached to the log. The

Duplex Loaders

To successfully load by the Duplex Loading System, it is necessary to use a special type of loading engine. This engine is similar to the cargo winches used on shipboard. The drums are keyed rigidly to the shaft, and the engine runs in either direction, controlled by a reverse valve. Each drum has an entirely independent set of engines, so that each line is operated independently of the other.

Operators who employ this type loader in their operations recognize the fact that little or no delay is experienced in landing the logs at the spar tree. The speed of this system enables the loader to operate continuously without hampering the yarding operations.

Loading logs with a Duplex.

Control levers for operating from right hand side.

front end of the log was broken out of the pile and suspended until it was free. The other tong was then fastened to the other end of the log, and as this end was lifted from the ground, the log would swing directly over the center of the car, ready to be lowered into place.

These machines became very popular in the 1920s, and were used as sled-mounted loaders and on many car-mounted units. "Duplex" loaders were built by Willamette Iron & Steel Works, Washington Iron Works, Smith & Watson Iron Works, and Puget Sound Iron & Steel Works. Unfortunately, no duplex loaders have survived the scrapper's torch in Oregon. At least two have been preserved in Washington State - a fine Washington Iron Works "duplex" on public display in Sedro-Wooley, Washington, and another at Camp 6 Logging Museum at Point Defiance Park in Tacoma, Washington. *Both pages from 1925 Willamette Iron & Steel Works Logging Machinery Catalog; Collection of Glen Comstock*

Duplex Loading

WHEN logging by any overhead or high-lead system, a special method of loading can be used to advantage, as the logs do not come to the landing parallel with the track. Where the spar tree is located adjacent to the track, the necessity of building a landing can be avoided by the use of the Duplex Loading System.

In this method of loading, two loading blocks are located on guy lines directly over the center of the car to be loaded, and two sets of loading lines are used.

In operation the tongs are carried out to the log and the front end of the log broken out of the pile and suspended until it is free. The other tongs are then fastened to the back end of the log, and as this end is lifted from the ground the log swings parallel to the car, directly over the center of it. It can then be lowered into place without any jar or racking to the equipment, and with the least amount of danger to the men. This method of loading is capable of very high speed operation, and in most cases will keep pace with any yarder.

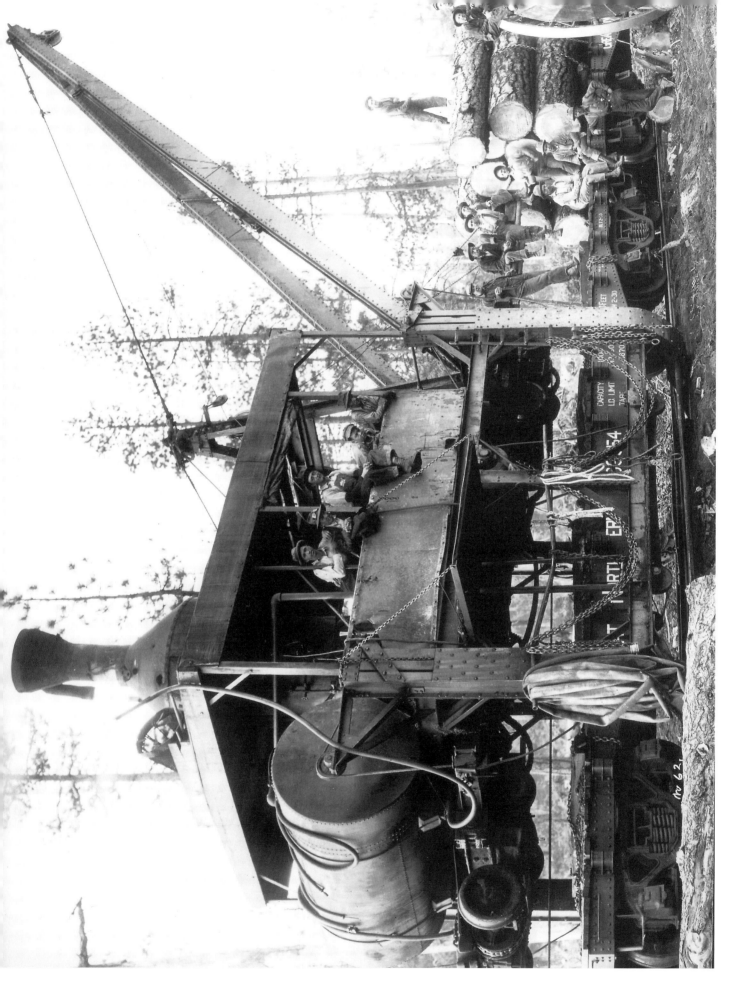

In Search of Steam Donkeys

CHAPTER 5

McGiffert Loaders

As railroad logging progressed, the loggers were looking for more efficient methods of loading railroad cars. In areas where logging of small timber was carried on, such as the Klamath Basin of south central Oregon, the steam "jammer" became a popular loading machine.

Walt McCulloch* lists the McGiffert loader as "A loading jammer used in pine logging; the last of the big old-time railroad machines. This loader came into the West Coast woods from the South. It was probably one of the best known loaders of this type."

Opposite   This beautiful Clark Kinsey photograph shows an eight-wheel McGiffert loader owned by Forest Lumber Company of Pine Ridge, Oregon, sometime in the 1930s. Note the protective covers on the big wheels, and the binding chains and hose draped all over the machine.   *C. Kinsey photo, courtesy of Martin E. Hansen*

---

*   Walter F. McCulloch, *Woods Words*, Oregon Historical Society and Champoeg Press, 1958, p 117.(Editor's note: The McGiffert loader was originally developed for pine logging in the Lake States. Its use in the South came later.)

These two Clark Kinsey photographs show the gradual transition from the use of big wheels to arches in pine logging. Logging with big wheels with tractors was an adaptation of horse logging, while the arches were designed specifically for tractors. The steel arches proved to be more versitile and durable.

Above Ewauna Box Company, of Lumberton, Oregon, near Klamath Falls, operated from 1924 to 1948, when they were taken over by Weyerhaeuser.

Left Lamm Lumber Company McGiffert loader and early cat and big wheel show. Note the guards on the insides of the wheel spokes. Lamm operated 50 miles of railroad out of Modoc Point, north of Klamath Falls, from 1915 to 1944. *Both C. Kinsey photos from Martin E. Hansen Collection*

Right Forest Lumber Company of Sprague River, Oregon. This Clark Kinsey view was taken some time after 1929. This is a large, swiveling, steel-boom, eight-wheel McGiffert loader. These machines were capable of yarding as well as loading. *Clark Kinsey photograph from Martin E. Hansen Collection*

Below Pelican Bay Lumber Company was a Weyerhaeuser subsidiary operating out of Algoma, Oregon. Here one of their large, modern steel McGifferts loads short logs onto very short skeleton cars *Martin E. Hansen Collection*

Above   The sign in this photo of Machine No. 40 above reads: *"People who produce more so that there is more to divide among all of us really move America ahead. Gift of Cap Collier."* This McGiffert loader has a Brooks-Scanlon log car spotted under it.   *All photos of Machine No. 40, 1977, Merv Johnson*

Early Stiff Boom McGiffert Loader

The following information is from the records of Cap Collier's camp, which is now a part of the Oregon State Highway Parks Division.

Machine No. 40 is a McGiffert loader manufactured by Clyde Iron Works in Duluth, Minn. in 1906. Patent date engraved on this hoist is 1902. Its original cost was $5,750. These loaders were called "jammers" by the loggers. The stiff boom type was a forerunner of those with swivel booms. McGiffert loaders were most widely used between 1906 and 1920 for loading on railroad cars. They may be moved under their own power. The McGiffert's wheels retracted up when in the loading mode to allow empty log cars to be pulled under and through the loader. This machine weighs over 100,000 lbs. and stands 30 feet high.

The stiff boom McGiffert replaced the "slide back"* loader which occupied one unloaded car and then would slide to

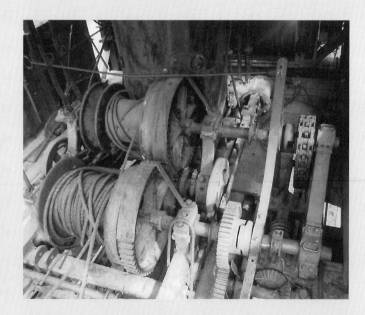

---

*   Although terminology and other information listed on this page was extracted from camp records and is as accurate as possible, it is not directly quoted. For example, loggers had a more colorful name for the term "slideback loader." Also, reference to boiler modifications are liberties taken by the author.

another as loads were completed (see photo on page 212). Log decks had to be spotted alongside the track and selection of logs was limited. The "slide back" was used quite extensively in Idaho. It is further reported that in Klamath, loading progressed from horse crosshaul to McGifferts with a minimum number of "slide back" loaders in the development of loading methods.

Machine No. 40 was first used by the McCloud River Lumber Co. of McCloud, California in early 1907. It was later used by Kesterson Lumber Co near Dorris, California and finally by Weyerhaeuser Lumber Co. in 1929, in Klamath Falls, Oregon. This was beyond the period in which these stiff-boom McGifferts were commonly used.

The McGiffert loader represented a giant step forward in log loading. These machines straddled a railway track and log cars were pushed under into loading position; then the logs were swung aboard. With a six man crew a McGiffert could load about 100,000 board feet per day at from 5,000 to 7,000 feet per car. Actual daily output in board feet for the McGiffert depended on the proficiency of its crew. The Pelican Bay Lumber Company crew once loaded 560,000 board feet of pine in an eight hour day, near Crater Lake, Oregon. This is believed to be a world's record for an eight-hour shift with a stiff-boom McGiffert used under normal working conditions. In one of the spectacular demonstrations (definitely not a normal operation) "so dearly loved by the Walker Brothers at Westwood, California," they yarded 1,000,000 board feet in a one day operation. The cost to the company was not made public, but it was a great day with movie stars and all the top brass of California present.

Machine No. 40 is listed as standard gauge, 19 feet long, 13 feet wide. Clearance height for cars to pass under is 5'2". One of its three drums is missing. There was 250 ft. of 5/8" cable on the front and rear drums and 500 ft. of 5/8" cable on the middle drum. The front drum was equipped with a gypsy. It had hand drums for side guys with hand ratchet guying drums. The original boiler was 102" high (which may mean a change in boilers was made somewhere along the way, since the author's measurements give it a height of 116"). The water tank is 54"x96"; boiler pressure: 150 lbs. The records show the following equipment upon delivery: Three tongs at 28", 36" and 42". Loading hooks: four pair special, and one pair double hook. Blocks: two guying, and two skidding blocks.

Additional Data:
1-1/2" steam supply pipe
2" exhaust
Fire door 9-1/2" x 14-1/2"
Stephenson reversing valve gear.
5" wide extra flange on haulback drum. The front drum has been removed, but the brackets are still there.
There is a takeoff shaft on the haulback drum that contains the sprocket that chain-drives the rail wheels.
Raising and lowering are accomplished by driving bevel and worm gears from the main drum shaft.

OWNER	Collier Logging Museum				Machine
Location	Chiloquin, Oregon				#40
Builder	Clyde Iron Works S/N 678				
Type	McGiffert Log Loader				
Bore & Stroke	9 x 10				

	D	W	L	THICK	H
FRAME SIZE		60	128	6	11
PINION GEAR	6-1/2	2-1/2			
CRANK DISC	21	2-1/2			
BOILER	42				116

	FLANGE DIA	CORE D/W	GEAR & BRAKE PD	F/ WIDTH	SHAFT DIA
MAIN DRUM	28	13/23	31	4-1/2	3-3/4
MAIN DOG	24			2	
H/B DRUM	25	13/17	31	4-1/2	3-3/4

Machine No. 41 was a "real challenge" to move to its present location at the Collier Logging Museum at Chiloquin, Oregon. It was cut up in sections and moved on lowboys. It was then reassembled with the help of cranes and welded back together again.

We owe Cap Collier a debt of gratitude for his efforts to build this elaborate museum.

Machine No. 41 at the Collier Logging Museum. Sign reads: "Late swingboom McGiffert log loader built by Clyde for Big Lakes Box *(of Klamath Falls, Oregon)* in 1926. Used by Palmerton Lumber Company in 1947 and Weyerhaeuser Timber Co. until 1961. *'May you also enjoy honorable retirement after a life full of work for your fellow man.'* Gift of Lowell Jones, Grant March, Ernie Barst, G.M. Uppington, Weyerhaeuser, and Cap Collier." At Collier Museum. *Author's photos*

Additional Data:
The middle drum has a five-inch wide strawline drum located on the engineer's side attached.
The boom swing is powered by a 17 inch diameter piston.
Valve gear is reversing Stephenson.
2-1/2" steam supply pipe.
American steam pump, Marsh style.
Collier Museum, Merv Johnson

OWNER Location Builder Type Bore & Stroke	Collier Logging Museum Chiloquin, Oregon Clyde Iron Works McGiffert Log Loader S/N 1281 9 x 10 Engine S/N 7683				Machine #41
	D	**W**	**L**	**THICK**	**H**
FRAME SIZE		60	130	5-1/2	13 (varies)
PINION GEAR	6				
CRANK DISC	21	2-1/2			
BOILER	42				114
	FLANGE DIA	**CORE D/W**	**GEAR & BRAKE** **PD F/ WIDTH**		**SHAFT DIA**
FRONT DRUM	28	/22	32	4-1/2	3-3/4
FRONT DOG	25-1/2			2	
REAR DRUM	28	/19-1/2	31	4-1/2	3-3/4
REAR DOG	26			2	
MID DRUM	25	13/18	31	4-1/2	3-3/4
MID DOG	24			2	

Left This 1962 view shows a McGiffert loading the last car, ending 80 years of railroad logging for Weyerhaeuser Timber Co. at Klamath Falls, Oregon. *John Labbe Collection*

Above Cut from undated Clyde McGiffert loader sales catalog showing drive mechanism for eight-wheel model. *Glen Comstock Collection*

Right Catalog cut showing boom swiveling mechanism. *Glen Comstock Collection*

Below A Pelican Bay Lumber Co. McGiffert loading pine logs with Shay locomotive standing by. *Jack Holst Collection from John Labbe*

In Search of Steam Donkeys

Above Machine No. 42 at Beaver Marsh, Oregon. Unfortunately, this eight-wheel McGiffert loader was scrapped in 1978. *Author's photo, circa 1975*

M achine No. 42 is one of only two machines in this book that was originally equipped with boiler lagging. The other one, a Tacoma yarder, is in the Collier Logging Museum, a few miles away, at Chiloquin, Oregon.

Unfortunately, this machine was scrapped in the early years that information was being collected for this book. It was located at Beaver Marsh near a mill close to the Southern Pacific railroad, south of Bend, Oregon. Attempts by the author to establish ownership of the machine prior to scrapping were discouraging, to put it mildly.

This loader was scrapped in 1978. It is nevertheless included here to show the jeopardy all these machines are in. Part of the motivation for creating this book is to publicize the fact that the few remaining traces of our logging heritage should be preserved. Those who have an affinity for these machines as concrete artifacts of logging history are disturbed upon realizing that the scrapper's torch is still a threat to these few remaining machines.

Machine No. 42 data:

Engine - 9 x 10   s/n 6696
NY & Boston Boiler 44-1/2" diameter x 96" tall
with lagging 96" high
Steam operated swivel on boom.
Knee operated, 40 feet long Slack puller on right side.
Knowles pump #128009110 Patent June 20, 1899
4 1/2 x 2-3/4" x 4"
House: 11' high x 13'-5" wide

Below A McGiffert loader of Weyerhaeuser Timber Co. of Bly, Oregon, 1956. *Martin E. Hansen Collection*

Hood and Stack

McGiffert Loader Hoist Engine Parts List

1. Steam Chest Cover	33. Ratchet	98. Drum Shaft
2. Cylinder	34. Drum	152. Small Segment Gear
3. Cylinder Jacket	36. Drum Gear	153. Large Segment Gear
4. Back Cylinder Head	38. Gear Guard	155. Reverse Lever
5. Front Cylinder Head	41. Pawl for Forward Drum	156. Reverse Lever Quadrant
6. Cross Head Guide	42. Crank Shaft Bearing Cap	178. Boiler Hood & Stack
7. Piston Rod Gland	43. Pawl for Rear Drum	179. Rim for Smoke Stack
8. Piston Rod w/Head	44. Hand Hole Crab & Plate	180. Lid for Smoke Stack
9. Cross Head Guide Bracket	45. Boiler Rod, Long	181. Bracket for Stack Lid
10. Connecting Rod	46. Boiler Rod, Short	182. Handle for Stack Lid
12. Drain Cock Lever Shaft	47. Throttle Valve Handle	183. Bracket for Stack Lid Handle
13. Drain Cock Lever Socket	49. Throttle Valve Rod	184. Angle Bracket for Boiler Hood
20. Large Side Stand	50. Glass Water Gauge	185. Thrust Lever Rest
22. Crank Disc	51. Steam Gauge	186. Gear Guard Stand
24. Thrust Screw	52. Whistle	187. Water Glass Gauge Cock
25. Thrust Lever	53. Safety Valve	188. Angle Valve
26. Thrust Nut	54. Lubricator	189. Cylinder Drain Cocks
27. Small Side Stand	55. Bracket for Lubricator	330. Half Clutch Gear for Truck Raising
28. Bed	56. Throttle Valve	331. Half Clutch for Truck Raising
29. Drum Shaft Bearing Cap	57. Coupling for Throttle Valve Rod	332. Set Collar
30. Thrust Bar	58. Injector	335. Shifting Lever
31. Push Collar	67. Eccentric Strap	336. Half Clutch Sprocket for Propelling
32. Grease Cup Holder		462. Shifting Lever

Above   Catalog cuts showing wheel lifting mechanisms for both four and eight-wheel McGifferts.

Above left   Parts breakdown for Clyde hoist engine used for McGiffert loaders.

Below   A McGiffert guyline hand winch.

All views on this page are from a Clyde Iron Works catalog (undated).   Glen Comstock Collection

McGiffert Loader, Western type, for skidding and loading, using cable for haul back.

Pages from an undated Clyde Iron Works catalog. The lower page shows a Brooks-Scanlon Lumber Company McGiffert loader. *Glen Comstock Collection*

McGiffert Loader, with swinging boom, showing clearing of cars when lifting the log.

Below McGiffert rigging diagram taken from a Broderick & Bascom Rope Co. Catalog, 1939. McGiffert loaders were sometimes used for yarding short distances as well as for loading, but this diagram doesn't add up to anything operational. It is known that some of the catalogs portrayed misleading information. *Steven Gatke Collection*

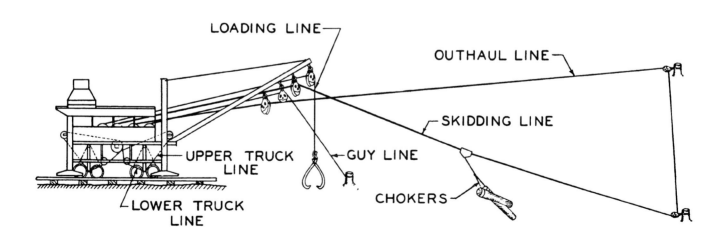

LOADING LINE

OUTHAUL LINE

SKIDDING LINE

UPPER TRUCK LINE

GUY LINE

CHOKERS

LOWER TRUCK LINE

McGIFFERT LOADER AND SKIDDER

Above   Brooks-Scanlon Lumber Company McGiffert loader working a truck-to-railroad reload out of their Sisters, Oregon Camp, 1952. An interesting contrast is the wood-burning McGiffert working alongside modern diesel trucks.   *Martin E. Hansen Collection*

Below   An earlier Brooks-Scanlon view, this one taken at their Bull Springs Camp between Bend and Sisters, Oregon. Brooks-Scanlon was a large operation, with their headquarters and sawmill in Bend, Oregon. They operated many camps in the Central Oregon Cascades, and were a leading producer of pine lumber for many years.   *Martin E. Hansen Collection*

In Search of Steam Donkeys

Above   Medford Corporation (Medco) was another large pine operation in Oregon. They operated out of Butte Falls, near Medford, Oregon.   *Martin E. Hansen Collection*

Below   Another Medco. Corp. view, showing a Medco McGiffert working a truck-to-rail reload about 1940. Note the two Clyde 4-line double-ended skidders down the track, the old passenger coach, and the No. 4, a Willamette locomotive.   *Martin E. Hansen Collection*

McGiffert Loaders

inning incline 66⅔% grade.

In Search of Steam Donkeys

CHAPTER 6
INCLINE ENGINES

Incline engines (also referred to as lowering engines and snubbers) were used to move railroad cars up and down rails too steep to negotiate with locomotives.

Although usually equipped with only one large drum, these machines nevertheless probably held the record for the largest component dimensions used on steam donkeys. Gear, drum, and bore and stroke dimensions were of record size.

Inclines were fairly common in the Northwest, although more so in Washington than in Oregon. Having an incline was considered a sign of prestige among timber operators.

Left "Logging incline on 66-1/2% grade at Wisconsin Logging and Timber Co., Columbia River, Washington." *Clark Kinsey photo, Lee Johnson collection*

YEON & PELTON INCLINE

Three loads nearing the bottom at Yeon and Pelton incline, Rainier, Oregon. This operation used a 16 x 20 engine especially built to lower loads down the steep incline to the bottom land of the Columbia River. Lee Johnson has identified the men from left to right as "Blondie" Frederickson, Harry Frederickson, and Joe David; also that the Spring freshet always flooded the bottom land in the early 1900s. Yeon and Pelton's railroad was 42 inch (bastard) gauge.   *Lee Johnson collection*

In Search of Steam Donkeys

Above This was Yeon & Pelton's first incline engine, installed in 1902. It used hydraulics to control the descent of loaded cars and an auxiliary steam engine to bring the empties back up the hill. Robert Johnson, the author's grandfather, is standing behind the crank disk. *John Labbe Collection*

The water cylinders (K) are closed at both ends and are connected with the pipe (L) which has a plug valve (M) near the middle. When (M) is closed the water is confined and holds the pistons (H) rigidly in place. Opening the valve (M) allows the water to pass alternately from one end of the cylinder to the other, the speed being governed by the extent to which the valve is opened. The controlling levers are so arranged that the valves (M) can only be opened and closed gradually, thus avoiding heavy shocks on the cable. In addition to the hydraulic cylinder brakes the machine is equipped with emergency brake bands and wooden friction blocks. The cable and empty cars are returned to the head of the incline by an auxiliary steam-driven engine.

Illustration and text taken from *Logging*, by Ralph Clement Bryant, 1923, John Wiley & Sons *Philip Schnell Collection*

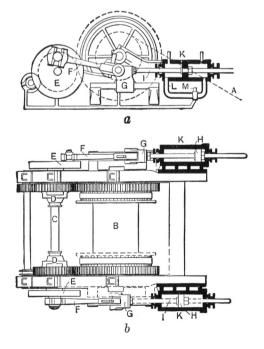

Incline Engines

Willamette Iron & Steel Works called this incline donkey the largest logging engine on earth, according to a news note in the February 1903 *Timberman*. This is the 16 x 20 Willamette that eventually replaced the engine shown on the previous page, and may well have had the largest bore and stroke of any logging donkey built. The length of Yeon & Pelton's incline was 3200 feet, with a grade from 14% to 33%. When lowering three cars at a time, pressure was calculated to be 600 pounds per square inch. The hydraulic system was tested at 1,000 psi, and was equipped with ten manually operated brakes. Some of the concrete foundation was still on site in the 1980s. Left to right in the photograph are Robert Johnson, fireman (Lee's father), Andrew Peterson, and Hugh Platt. *The Timberman* for January, 1903 carried an article on this incline. Credits for this information to Lee Johnson (author's father) who lived there at the time, and *The Timberman*.   *Lee Johnson collection*

Right   Yeon & Pelton incline looking up from the log dump at the bottom. There is a man riding on each car. The house at the top of the bluff on the left was owned by the author's grandfather, Robert Johnson. See story on page 48.   *John T. Labbe Collection*

In Search of Steam Donkeys

BENSON TIMBER COMPANY INCLINE

This incline was located out of Clatskanie, Oregon about five or six miles above "Swede Town" near "Upper Camp." The rail spur on the left goes toward camp. The railway was the long way around to camp and was used for various reasons such as bringing in heavy equipment. The incline was used as the shorter route to deliver logs from camp. All logs were hauled on disconnected trucks. The steam appearing on the left is coming from the water pump used to supply the incline donkey on top by means of a water pipe up the hill. The pump operator lived by the pump. Whistles from above provided signals for the operations. The two-room cabin across from the pump was occupied by the aunt and uncle of Rudy Larson. As was the custom, the crew was lowered down the incline on a flatcar each day. The incline engineer allowed the car to coast about two-thirds of the way down, then applied the brakes. Unfortunately, a prankster once greased the brake band on Halloween night. Needless to say, the car did not slow as expected the next day. Realizing the danger, the crew bailed out before the car left the tracks. Fortunately, no one was killed, but broken bones were suffered that fateful day. The prankster was never found out. *Notes from Rudy Larson. Rudy's father, Albin, was woods foreman for Benson Timber Co. Clark Kinsey photograph courtesy of Martin E. Hansen*

This is another Clark Kinsey photograph taken at the top of the Benson Timber Company incline pictured on the previous page. The donkey in the foreground is used as the incline machine to pull the loads up. The donkey behind was not in use at the time, and to the best of Rudy Larson's knowledge was maintained as a standby. Firewood to fuel the donkey was subcontracted out and hauled in with the horse shown. *Photo and information from Rudy Larson.*

Pioneer Donkey Hunters

by Philip Schnell

Robert and Fred Wenzel can probably make the claim to be among the very first of the "wild donkey hunters." Way back in 1950 the two brothers and a friend heard of a steam donkey abandoned in a remote area of Oregon's Coast Range. What they found in subsequent trips were the burned-out remains of the West Oregon Lumber Company's incline and camp. Their prize was a large Washington Iron Works incline engine perched at the top of one of the world's steepest logging inclines. The incline at one time reached from the depths of the Salmonberry Canyon near Belding, Oregon on the SP Tillamook Branch, to high up on a ridge, were the camp was located and the logging railroad wandered back into the hills.

West Oregon Lumber Company was a longtime producer

Left and above These two photos were taken by H. Mack, who was Bridge & Building foreman for SP. This was shortly after the 1932 fire, as the embers are still smoldering. The left view is looking west from east of the upper end of Tunnel No. 32 on the line. The picture above shows the trestle work at the bottom of the incline. The track to the right connects to the SP line to Portland. The left track connects to the Tillamook-bound line. *H. Mack photos from Darel Mack, courtesy of Robert and Fred Wenzel*

of lumber in the Portland area. They operated a large mill at Linnton, Oregon, near Portland. In order to maintain their supply of timber, in 1929 they purchased a tract of fine old-growth yellow fir, deep in the Salmonberry Canyon, high above the SP's Tillamook Branch. The incline, logging railroad and camp were built in 1930. A very steep incline was the only practical way to get the timber out, and this one was a dandy, reaching a grade of as much as 83% with a difference in elevation of 1430 feet. This was a counterbalanced incline, using two sets of tracks and a large "gypsy"

type lowering engine to lower loads and raise empties simultaneously, the lower portion on gauntlet track. At the bottom, the incline split into a wye and connected with the SP Tillamook Branch. The wye straddled tunnel No. 32. Extensive trestlework was required at the bottom where it clung to the steep banks of the Salmonberry River.

In 1932, a forest fire swept through the canyon, and destroyed the timber, logging railroad, incline, and camp of West Oregon Lumber Company. (This fire may have caused the demise of Machine No. 28. See page 85.) Due to the remoteness of the area, and difficulty of access, after salvage of the other equipment, the huge Washington Iron Works 12 x 14 lowering engine was left sitting at the top of the incline until sometime in the fifties, when it was finally retrieved for scrap.

Right A view from near the top of the West Oregon Incline. The 12x14 Washington Iron Works lowering engine sat nearby. *Fred Wenzel photograph, 1951*

Below and right During a subsequent visit in 1953, Fred Wenzel, left, and Lee Schneider, examine the 12x14 Washington Iron Works lowering engine at the head of the incline. This 1923 engine had been owned previously by The Whitney Company and used on the incline at their Blue Star Camp out of Idaville, Oregon. (See page 191.) *Robert Wenzel photographs*

Smith-Powers Logging Company operated this incline at their Camp 6, near Powers, Oregon. Note that the cable appears to be connected to the logs and not the car. Smith-Powers built most of their railroad on low trestlework, due to the soft, unstable ground in the Coos Bay area.   *Clark Kinsey photo, Martin E Hansen Collection*

In Search of Steam Donkeys

Left   The Mundy incline engine built for Apex Transportation Co. at Bridal Veil. *Courtesy of John T. Labbe*

Below   The Apex incline at Bridal Veil. *The Timberman, Jan., 1937.*

BRIDAL VEIL INCLINE AND BULL DONKEY

The Bridal Veil Lumber Co., located on the Columbia River east of Portland, Oregon, was formed in 1887 by L.C. Palmer, C. Brown, and T.H. Smith. The accompanying community of Bridal Veil formed soon after, and became the site of the planing mill and yards. The mill in the town of Palmer, two miles from Bridal Veil, cut cants and fed the company's flume. Palmer was also the home of the loggers and the people who worked at the upper end of the lumber flume; from 30 to 35 families resided there all year. A lack of transportation facilities kept these people separated from the outside world. The isolation forged strong links among their citizens through lodge meetings and through social events held at the school building, such as dances, literary society meetings, spelling bees, and community dinners.

In January 1937, after 50 years of operation, Bridal Veil announced plans to close its plant, sell its equipment, and vacate its two towns.

Apex Transportation Company was the logging contractor for Bridal Veil Lumber Company. Apex used oxen or horses for logging until about 1896; however, because of the harsh terrain on Larch Mountain, a cable system, designed along the lines of the San Francisco cable car system, was built for Apex by the J.S. Mundy company of Chicago. Cables were wound on two large drums, and the donkey, supplied by two boilers, could haul 30,000 feet of logs (120,000 lbs). This system was capable of reaching out a mile and a half, but the main chute was three quarters of a mile. This endless cable in the main chute pushed logs uphill end-to-end until they reached the top, where gravity completed the journey down the chute on the other side. The logs descended 300 feet in a lateral distance of 1200 feet, making tremendous sprays as they hit the water.

The parts of the bull donkey shown at right were built by

Mundy, and are the oldest donkey parts yet found in Oregon. These few remains are of a donkey used by Donahue and Kelly, subcontractors for Bridal Veil Timber Co. near Palmer's camp in the Bridal Veil area. Their operations started in 1881 and ended in 1896 [according to Lewis Faught (right side in photo)].

Below   The remains shown were the snubbing unit for the machine shown at top left. Logs were yarded to the top of a chute, then sent down to a pond where they were handled by train (trailed) to the Palmer mill pond. The snubber was left behind when the donkey was moved, since it was no longer needed. The gear shown is 50 inches in diameter with a 7 inch face. Shaft diameter is 4-3/8 inches. The other end of the shaft features a wheel with five grooves in it. [Thanks to Tom Nelson (left) John Labbe (center) and Lewis Faught (right) for finding these fragments.] *Author's photo, 1984*

*A Willamette engine hauling itself
up an incline under its own steam*

Gypsy Type

All Willamette hoisting or lowering engines are equipped with specially designed brakes cooled by a flow of water against the band. One brake is operated by compound hand levers from a quadrant and the other controlled by compressed air. One set of brake blocks, when given the proper care, will last for several years.

Particular attention is called to the drum construction of the Gypsy type lowering engine. The cable winding space between the gear and the Gypsy permits the engine being moved into its setting under its own power. Occasionally lowering engines are shipped from the shops loaded on

*Specially designed brake control
of Willamette Hoisting and
Lowering engines.*

Pages 186 through 190 are taken from the 1925 Willamette Iron & Steel Catalog, and illustrate the different types of incline engines the firm offered. The illustrations on this page show the incline operation of Porter-Carstens Logging Co. of Estacada, Oregon. *Glen Comstock Collection*

flat cars in such a manner as to enable their being hauled up the incline under their own steam.

Frequently the length of incline is such that in order to obtain the necessary capacity in number of cars handled per day, an empty must ascend at the same time that a load descends. In this case the so-called Gypsy type of lowering engine is used. The line, instead of coiling on the drum, has two or three wraps around the Gypsy. The engine is equipped with reversing valve gear so that it may operate in either direction.

At the same time a load is lowered an empty car is raised, the two passing at the half-way point on the incline. The empty car thus acts as a counter balance against the load being lowered, reducing the amount of work required of the engine brakes.

As most incline operations extend over a period of years, occasionally the incline hoist is mounted on a concrete foundation, as is customary in mine hoist practice. By so mounting, the hoist is relieved of all vibrations and strains due to poor setting on sled.

Illustrating concrete setting.

The Sessom's System

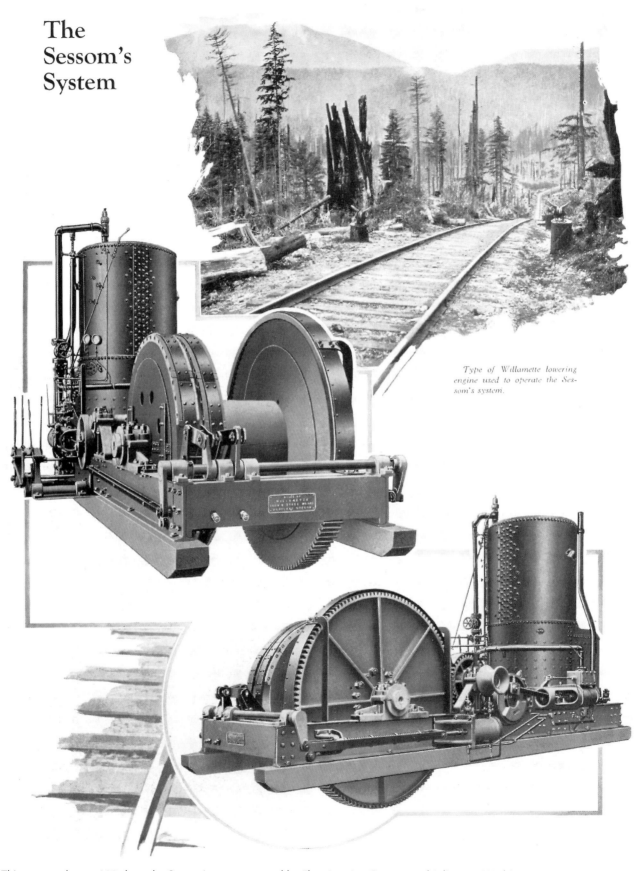

Type of Willamette lowering engine used to operate the Sessom's system.

This page and page 189 show the Sessom's system as used by Ebey Logging Company of Arlington, Washington.

In Search of Steam Donkeys

LOWERING AND HOISTING ENGINES

Switching logs with block car.

THIS type of hoisting and lowering engine is used where a particularly large rope capacity is required. For this reason it is used extensively for operating the Sessom's system. This engine is also equipped with reverse valve gear to permit feeding of slack.

The Sessom's system of lowering logs incorporates the principle of a block purchase on the loads. The line is passed from the drum on the engine through a series of large diameter sheaves mounted on the deck of a specially constructed steel car to an anchor on the side of the track opposite the lowering engine.

Sessom's system operates with minimum line wear.

A particular advantage possessed by this system lies in the fact that it is possible to operate on sharp curves.

Line guides and retainers are used throughout the length of the grade, both on curves and tangents to keep the cable from dragging on the ground. The line wear is, therefore, greatly decreased.

Due to the block purchase secured on the loads by means of the Sessom's car, lighter cable can be used than would otherwise be the case.

Block car at top of incline.

Tandem Drum Type

The Tandem Drum type of lowering engine is similar in general arrangement to a road engine, with the exception that the frame and main drum are liberally designed to take care of the peculiar loads that come upon them and to provide for substantial braking capacity. The additional drum may be used for a variety of purposes, particularly switching cars at the terminal. This type is recommended where the lowering service is of a temporary nature as it can be also used for regular logging purposes.

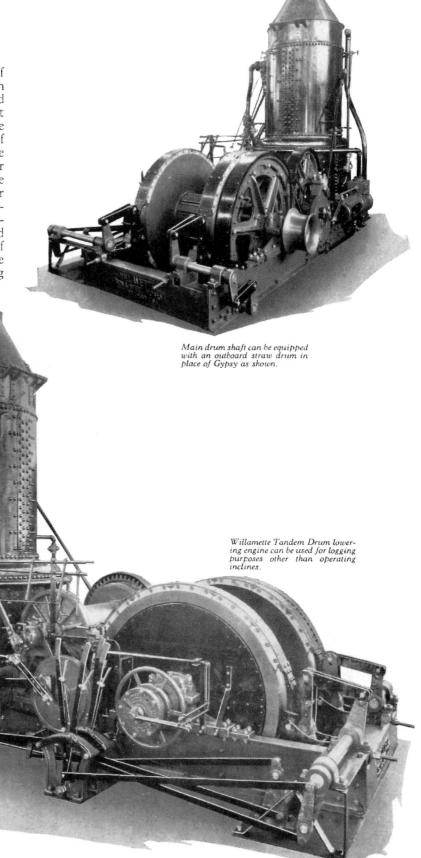

Main drum shaft can be equipped with an outboard straw drum in place of Gypsy as shown.

Willamette Tandem Drum lowering engine can be used for logging purposes other than operating inclines.

Right The Whitney Company operated several camps in the hills above Garibaldi and Idaville, Oregon. Their most famous camp, named "Blue Star," was located in a particularly rugged region of the Coast Range. To deal with the terrain, they constructed an enormous incline. This view shows the well-remembered "Molly-O," a three-truck Climax locomotive, taking a trip up the hill. Careful inspection reveals a man hanging on the engineer's side of the cab. When Whitney was done logging, the Washington Iron Works 12" x 14" lowering engine used on this incline was sold to West Oregon Lumber Company for use on their incline in the Salmonberry Canyon near Belding, Oregon. The engine sat there abandoned for many years following a forest fire in the area in 1932. (See page 182.) *Martin E. Hansen Collection*

Left This 13x13 lowering engine was offered by Smith & Watson Iron Works of Portland, Oregon. A quote from the undated catalog page reads: "Lowering engines are necessarily constructed to meet such a variety of conditions that no general type can be listed."
Author's Collection

In Search of Steam Donkeys

CHAPTER 7
MISCELLANEOUS RELATED STEAM EQUIPMENT

This chapter is devoted to items of steam logging equipment that didn't fit in the previous chapters, that were nevertheless important to the logging industry. Unfortunately, there are not surviving examples of every kind of equipment that was used in Oregon. The giants are gone. Steam logging, and the logging railroads, required a lot of support industries as shown by the seasonal and cyclical economic swings that affected the entire Northwest. Loggers were noted for their ability to adapt and change to conditions, which meant that a lot of equipment was either modified or home-built. This resulted in a variety of equipment, some of which is not widely known.

Opposite   Schafer Brothers Logging Company's Clyde track laying machine in action near Brady, Washington.
These machines were called "Japanese skidders" by the loggers.
Clark Kinsey photograph courtesy of Peter Replinger

Above   The author's son, Mike Johnson poses with these "torpedoes," as they were called. These tanks were filled with crude oil and sent out over land to the yarders that were a distance from the railroad by using the "swing" donkey via a high lead system. Using oil as fuel was a first step in the gradual process of reducing labor costs. These are at the Camp 18 Logging Museum near Elsie, Oregon.   *Author's photo, mid-1970s*

Below   Oil-fired donkeys no longer needed wood bucks to supply the fuel. The next development was an automatic oil burner, intended to eliminate the fireman.   *Lee Johnson photo, taken at Tidewater Timber Company during the steam era.*

In Search of Steam Donkeys

"S. & W." Oil Burner for Logging Engines

Burner

The burner used is one that perfectly mixes and atomizes the crude oil, affording an absolutely clean fire, without smoke or smudging of tubes.

Pump

The pump is specially fitted with metallic rings for oil. It is also equipped with a governor for automatically regulating oil pressure. The oil plant, including the heater, is compact and mounted on a separate cast iron bed on the back end of the sled near the boiler, making easy connections from pump to boiler.

Regulating System

The connections that control the steam and oil mixture are few and simple. All connecting pins are liberal in size and well fitted. The main connection between the controlling lever and the engine throttle is made with a 5/16-inch cable equipped with a turn buckle to allow for adjustment.

Above An oil burner system offered by Smith & Watson for use on logging engines. From a Smith & Watson Iron Works catalog, undated. *Author's Collection*

Below Oil and water tank from the same Smith & Watson Iron Works catalog. This tank was 5 feet in diameter and 8 feet long, with a capacity of 1175 gallons *Author's Collection*

Moxley

An Efficient, Self-Regulating Oil Burner

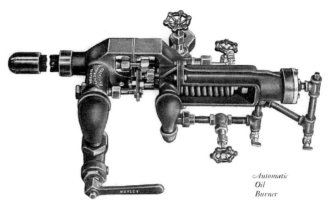

Automatic Oil Burner

The operation of the Moxley Automatic Oil Burner is simple and positive. This burner is of the inside mixing type. Steam from the steam manifold passes thru and is regulated by the steam valve No. 18. This steam draws the fuel oil thru fuel oil cock and thru the regulating oil valve No. 17 to the mixing chamber. From the mixing chamber the oil spray passes thru the burner tip No. 31 into the firebox. Both the oil valve No. 17 and the steam valve No. 18 are controlled and regulated by the steam cylinder No. 3. Boiler pressure steam is admitted to the back end of this cylinder No. 3 and moves the crosshead No. 16 towards the burner tip closing both valves. The boiler pressure necessary to shut off the oil supply is regulated by adjusting the spring No. 12. Steam from under the engine throttle is admitted to the front end of the cylinder, so that when the engine throttle valve is opened the burner instantly starts up regardless of the boiler pressure. In this way a full head of steam is maintained. (Numbers given are shown on blueprints).

Above From the *Moxley Oil Burning Equipment Catalog*, pg. 2. Manufactured by the Moxley Oil Burning Equipment Co., Inc, of Hoquiam, Washington. Date unknown. *from the Jim Gertz Collection*

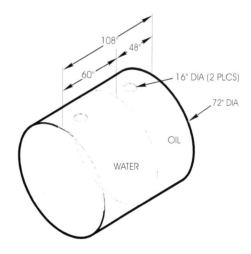

Above A water/fuel tank for a yarder. This tank was found in the woods in an area that was once logged by Oregon-American Lumber Co. This tank would be adequate for an 11 x 13 engine, but a 60" x 96" tank could also be used. See also sled plan on page 263. Not to scale. *Drawn by Philip Schnell*

Adams Spark Arrester

CONSTRUCTION

A specially designed and constructed stack.

Two cone-shaped screens within the stack.

One screen from the bottom of the stack to a hollow cast ring.

The other screen is inverted, extending downward within the first screen and just above the lower exhaust.

The screens being within the stack are protected from cold air, thus preventing the formation of oils and creosote over their surface.

Two exhaust pipes, one below and one above the screens, causes a blast which increases the draft and forces the sparks in a rasping motion along the screens, keeping them clear of soot.

The sparks are forced along the screens into a hollow cast ring. A spark outlet on either side, with spouts, convey the sparks into a barrel or container. The suction from upper exhaust above the screens overcomes back pressure.

After a careful study of the matter of "spark arresters," we have selected the "Adams" as a device which does all that is claimed for it in the way of preventing sparks from leaving the stack of a logging engine.

It will save the logger an untold amount of money by preventing the starting of fires.

We are prepared to install "Adams" arresters on any of our engines.

Quotations upon application.

From the *Smith & Watson Iron Works Catalog No. 9*, Date unknown. *Author's collection*

There is always plenty of work around a logging outfit. Here it looks as though the wood buck is keeping up. Simmons Brothers' logging operation at Simmons Creek, Tillamook County.   *Courtesy of Homer and Lorene Simmons*

A lot of straight-grained wood was used as fuel, The steamers were powerful, but it took a lot of fuel to keep them going.

Above   Since there is a drag saw in this Big Creek Logging Co. photo, the need for the hand saws is questionable. Perhaps the drag saw broke down, or maybe the cutting crew placed their hand saws there for the photo.   *Weister photo, OHS W.I.S.Co. Collection OrHi 92941*

Left   Big Creek Logging Company of Knappa, Oregon.   *Weister photo, Ockelman-Parker Collection*

Power dragsaws were quickly accepted by loggers as a means of reducing the labor required to produce fuel wood for their donkey engines.

Top right   This steam-powered dragsaw is shown near Silverton, Oregon. This type required a headframe as shown in the photograph.   *Steven Gatke Collection*

Middle right   This unidentified view shows an early gasoline-powered dragsaw. This is definitely not a machine for one man to tote around the woods.   *John T. Labbe Collection*

Bottom right   The most common type of gasoline dragsaw was this type, built by Wade, Vaughn, and a few others. Although hardly lightweight, advertisements often claimed that they could be carried by one man.   *Will Davis Collection*

Below   The caption on this photo reads: "pump man." This was another job phased out with the demise of steam power. The pump man's job was to look after the water supply. Providing a water supply also involved laying pipe, sometimes for great distances. In some places it was the donkey doctor's job to provide for water, or at least help out.   *Steven Gatke Collection*

Miscellaneous Related Steam Equipment

A Water Pump
Salvage Operation

Gasoline and diesel pumps were often used to pump water uphill to steam donkeys. This salvage operation occurred in the Oregon Coast Range area. This 1931 engine was disconnected from the pump and yarded 1000 feet up to the road.

Right   The reward after a hard day's salvage work was a cool drink and a 4,050 pound 15 h.p. two-cycle Fairbanks-Morse diesel. The crew on this job: Bill, Don, Kenny and Dolores Peterson; Kevin Warrick and Ed Bartholemy.

Below   The final restored product after several months work.

Author's photos, circa 1985

Miscellaneous Related Steam Equipment

OWNER Location Builder Type Bore & Stroke	Collier Logging Museum Chiloquin, Oregon Clyde Iron Works Track Laying Machine 5 x 6 s/n 133 engine s/n 6089				Machine #43
	D	W	L	THICK	H
PINION GEAR	5	3			
CRANK DISC	11-1/2	2			
	FLANGE DIA	CORE D/W	GEAR PD		
MAIN DRUM	21	11/12	23		
H/B DRUM	21	11/12	23		

Above   Machine No. 43, a Clyde track layer, on display at its current location, Collier Logging Museum near Chiloquin, Oregon. (editor's note—the ties have been incorrectly placed inside of this machine. In actual practice the ties would be placed on a separate flatcar.) *Author's photo, 1977*

CLYDE TRACK LAYING MACHINES

Machine No. 43, a Clyde track machine, was donated in 1963 by Cap Collier to the logging museum at Chiloquin, Oregon named in his honor. It was manufactured in 1923 by Clyde Iron Works, Inc. of Duluth, Minnesota. Known by loggers as "track layers," "Clyde track machines," or "Japanese skidders," it cost $4,895 new without flatcar. These machines were commonly used by loggers between 1923 and 1959. They had a knee-operated swing-boom. The steam supply came from a locomotive via a pipe running along the cars. Ties, rails, bridge timbers, and so forth were conveyed through the machine in either direction along a horizontal boom. All heavy lifting and carrying was done by the machine. The boom was 110 feet long. The frame was 25 feet long. Width of the frame at the base was 11 feet, 3 inches. Overall height was 27 feet. There was approximately 10 feet of clearance to stack ties on the car behind. Total weight was 24,000 pounds not including the flatcar carrying the

machine. The weight-carrying capacity of the trolley was 4,000 pounds.

The following has been excerpted from Cap Collier's Camp files verbatim:

From these dimensions you can see what a "bear cat" it was to move and reassemble. The equipment works on the single track as the laying or taking progresses, on fill, trestle, or cut with equal facility, and does not require any member of the crew to traverse the right of way at the side of any part of the equipment while attending the operation. A full crew of 15 to 17 men is used. This Swing Boom type allows you to center the load line, 2 chains with grab hooks for rails, 2 choker slings for ties, 36 bridle bars for holding rails to gauge, 3/8" wire rope for traffic and load lines, 2 sets metallic flexible steam connections, steam gauge, reducing valve, and a full compliment of tools.

In actual operation, it is a steam-powered crane mounted on a heavy railroad car with arms extending out over three cars. It could pick up a load of ties from the rear car, carry them forward and lay them down properly on the subgrade, then hold the weight until the fishplates were bolted. It was a very useful tool in the days when the railroad crept up every draw and then backed out and picked up its tracks behind it. Very few of our visitors will ever see again a railroad meandering off through the ginsengs, spitting out its tracks before it as it goes.

This track machine was purchased new by the Phoenix Logging Company (located near Shelton, Washington) on November 21, 1923. It was later sold to the Floyd Lamkin Machinery Company of Tacoma, Washington. On April 30, 1940, it was purchased by Weyerhaeuser Company of Klamath Falls, Oregon, where it operated until Cap Collier bought it in 1963 and paid all the costs of hauling and setting up this machine at its present display.

The twin of this machine is mentioned in issue 27 of *Timberbeast* Magazine and is still in existence near Big Lagoon, California. Both machines were shipped from Clyde on the same day. This one is machine No. 133, with hoist No. 6089, shipped to Willamette-Clyde on November 21, 1923.

Beside the track laying machines, Clyde Iron Works also manufactured the McGiffert Loaders shown elsewhere in this book.

These two rare photos show Machine No. 43, under Weyerhaeuser ownership, at work laying rails just north of their Sycan Shops, near Bly, Oregon. The locomotive is Weyerhaeuser Timber Co. No. 1, a Baldwin 2-8-2. The year was 1940.   *Martin E. Hansen Collection*

Below   Clyde track machine elevation drawing from Bill Roy and McKenzie Iron & Steel Works Plan Pack. *Not to scale.*

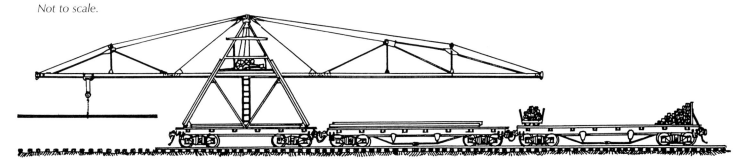

Miscellaneous Related Steam Equipment   203

Above A Clyde track layer somewhere in Western Washington State.   *Perkins photo, Steven Gatke Collection*

Below   This pile driver owned by Moore Mill & Lumber Company of Leneve, Oregon (near Bandon) has a hoist with a very large boiler. Pile drivers needed plenty of steam capacity because of their almost continuous operation. Abbey's Register lists Moore Mill & Lumber Co. as having one rod and two geared locomotives, 18 disconnects, operating on 6 miles of track. The Shay shown here was Lima c/n 3211, built in 1923.

In Search of Steam Donkeys

Above In addition to McGiffert loaders and track laying machines, Clyde Iron Works manufactured a wide range of unusual logging equipment, including this 4-line double-ended skidder owned by the Shevlin-Hixon Company. These fascinating machines were used in the semiarid pine regions. *Steven Gatke Collection*

Below Clyde 4-line double-ended skidder (s/n 368) owned by Medco sitting derelict at Butte Falls, Oregon. *Martin E. Hansen Collection*

Right A new sled for this Smith-Powers Logging Co. Willamette wide face roader. The condition of the old sled gives some idea of the abuse these machines were subjected to in the woods. *Clark Kinsey photograph from Martin E. Hansen Collection*

Below This amazing scene shows 90 donkey sleds under construction! This was the Spruce Division of the U.S. Army Signal Corps., who logged and milled airplane-grade spruce on a giant scale during World War I. Note the Shay bringing in a train of logs to use for more sleds. This view is at Toledo, Oregon. *Clark Kinsey photo from Martin E. Hansen*

In Search of Steam Donkeys

Donkey Sleds

Willamette Iron & Steel Works made several drawings of donkey sleds recommended for use with their machines. They had this to say about sleds:

Many loggers have their own ideas as to the proper construction of the sled for their logging engine. This drawing is offered as a suggestion for those seeking a satisfactory design. (From page 118 of their 1925 catalog, which includes a drawing.)

It became apparent that skimping on sled design was poor economy. The long length extending in front was an advantage, for example, when moving the donkey under its own power to negotiate variable terrain. The "snipe" or radius on both ends of the sled runners added strength to the runners and was an aid when going up or coming down from obstructions.

The type sled plate shown in photo A required a cable passed through the sled with eyes on both sides of the sled runner. This type always had slack on both ends, which was a disadvantage. The type shown in photo B and drawing C allowed more options by virtue of hooking up closer to the

sled. This arrangement allowed better steering when moving a donkey under its own power. The eye of the drum line was attached with a pin that went directly into the sled plate. One plate manufactured was a "Soule Sled Plate" which measured 14 x 22 inches and weighed 110 pounds.

While decking in the front is commonly visible, the area from the boiler to the rear of the sled can act as a substantial stabilizing force with decking. In many cases it was necessary to cut out a half-round area in one sled runner to allow clearance for the bull gear on the main drum. Drawing D shows end caps for mounting the fuel/water tank to the sled, which resemble a dado when mounted. Various methods were used to cradle the bottom of the tank and to prevent it from shifting from side to side. It could also be tied down with small cable and long eye bolts. For a sled plan, see page 263 of this book. The common sled plan in the W.I.S.Co. catalog mentioned above has appeared in several publications*. It is for larger donkeys, and shows a system of sway-braces, using diagonal rods. The rods required frequent adjustment. Not shown in either drawing is an alternate method of eliminating diagonal stress, which was to build in as much solid decking as possible.

Although sled building is presumably a lost art, we are fortunate that a few sleds have been built in recent times, including three that were built in the 1980s. The one in Tillamook (Machine No. 5) was built by Homer Simmons and his brothers; the other two (Machines No. 8 and 35) were built by Dean Smith. At press time, a fourth sled is being built at Reedsport, Oregon for Machine No. 36.

Photo A

Above   This sled requires a cable strap to go through the hole and out the other side.

Below   This type plate is used by attaching the eye of the cable and inserting a pin in the hole.   *Author's photos*   **Photo B**

Drawing C

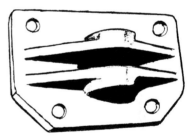

Above   Pin type sled plate.   *Drawn by the author*

Below   Fuel/water tank bracket.   *Drawn by Philip Schnell*

Drawing D

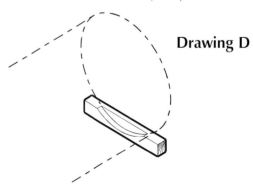

* *Timberbeast*, Issue No. 27, Fall, 1991

A study in sled construction, location unidentified. This Willamette yarder sports a sled with three fairleads: a large, roller type for the mainline, a bull's-eye type for the haulback, and a small through-the-headblock type for the strawline. The sled plates shown here are the kind requiring a hole in the sled runner through which a cable strap could pass. It was not uncommon to build sleds like this up to 65 feet in length. *Oregon Historical Society, W.I.S.Co. Collection, OrHi No. 92936*

In Search of Steam Donkeys

Above Donkey sled building somewhere on the Oregon Coast in the 1930s. Note the fellow on the ground with the hand-powered wheel auger. *Martin E. Hansen Collection*

Below Spar-jumping was a rare event in which a spar tree was moved a short distance without taking it down. This series of photographs was taken at Tidewater Timber Company of Jewell, Oregon. *John T. Labbe Collection*

Miscellaneous Related Steam Equipment

Spar Tree Raising

The raising of a wooden spar tree is rare in this day and age. A record crowd attended the spar tree raising that took place at Camp 18 Logging Museum near Elsie, Oregon on September 24, 1989. The tree will be used with two of the museum's steam donkeys to demonstrate yarding and loading as it was done in the age of steam logging. A "dummy" tree was used for lift to raise the 160-foot spar tree (see drawing). Most of those attending were retired loggers or those associated with logging history in some way. Enthusiasm ran high and the crowd applauded when the main spar tree was hoisted into position. Crew members were: John McMeekan, Leonard Foster, Keith Sweeney (high climbers); Bob Hawthorn, Tobey Ramey, Herb Olstedt, Denny Olstedt, Mark and Clay Smith, and Gordon Smith, owner.

Right The raised and partially-rigged spar tree at Camp 18 Logging Museum near Elsie, Oregon. *Author's photo*

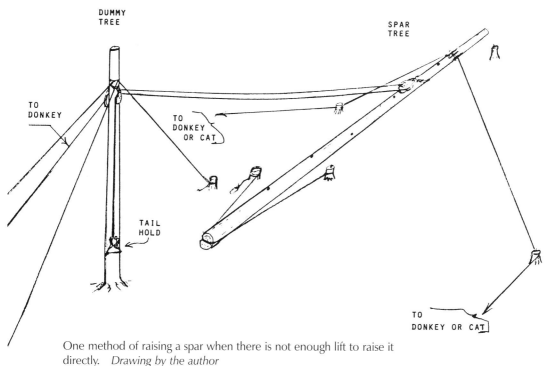

One method of raising a spar when there is not enough lift to raise it directly. *Drawing by the author*

Above   The booming operations of Deer Island Logging Company, on a backwater of the Columbia River. The Shay locomotive was built in 1906. Her previous owner was Clark Creek Logging Company of Kalama, Washington.   *Clark Kinsey photograph, Martin E. Hansen Collection*

Below   All of the major donkey manufacturers offered log unloading machines such as this one at the Valley & Siletz RR log dump at Independence, Oregon, shown here in 1948. The raft-mounted derrick in the background was for retrieving "sinkers."   *Guy Dunscomb photo from Martin E. Hansen Collection*

Miscellaneous Related Steam Equipment

Above Mt. Emily Lumber Company of La Grande, Oregon used this elderly slide-back steam loader right up to the end of operations. Here it's shown loading the last logs on the last train on June 20, 1955. *Martin E. Hansen Collection*

Below California & Oregon Lumber Company (previously Brookings Lumber Co.) operated out of Brookings, Oregon, on the southern Oregon Coast. In this 1922 view, several new Willamette donkeys are being prepared for operation. The No. 5, a Baldwin 2-6-2, c/n 55277 was also brand-new when this photograph was taken. *Martin E. Hansen Collection*

Right A steam-powered saw in Tillamook, Oregon, built by Gus Case and Allen Page. *Lee Johnson collection*

Logging has always been a task demanding creative solutions to constantly changing situations. Small wonder, then, that the equipment would reflect the loggers as innovators. This wheeled "vehicle" was homemade by a logger in Humboldt County, California. Note the flashing on the smokestack, the sloping wooden roof, and the vertical cylinder. Steering was accomplished by rotating the horizontal gear in front, much like the later Holt steam tractors. *Photo courtesy of John Labbe*

Miscellaneous Related Steam Equipment

An Afternoon with Rudy Larson

Fond memory brings the light
Of other days around me:
The smiles, the tears,
Of boyhood's years,

(T. Moore, "Oft In The Stilly Night")

It is fortunate that Rudy Larson took an interest in preserving a part of logging history. As a boy, Rudy lived in Benson Timber Compay's camp out of Clatskanie, Oregon. Fortunately, he still has photographs that were taken circa 1920. Of his photographs, some of which are shown in this book, many names are available upon request. An afternoon with Rudy unfolded an eye-witness account from the perspective of a small boy in a big camp:

The fact that my father was a logger from 1910 to 1939 made me aware of what logging was all about and the character of the people working in the woods of the time. Try to imagine (or remember) an era of steam as the primary source of power. Locomotives and donkeys were steam-powered. No chain saws.

Transportation into the high elevations of upper Clatskanie was by rail only. How different it is today, where one will find an airstrip near the area of Camp Nine, and the numerous roads for fire control purposes, some only accessible by four-wheel-drive.

The reason I knew many of the employees was because I was the only child in camp for a number of years, and my father was woods foreman. What does a child do without playmates? For one thing, my father (Albin) would take me to the commissary in the evenings. Sometimes I would come out of there with my mouth and pockets bulging with candy. It's a wonder I have a tooth in my mouth today. Some kids have a natural interest in machinery. I guess that included me. I was fascinated by steam. Whenever I got a chance, I would get up in the cab of lokeys, especially when the engineer would fire up the engines to hold steam overnight. We had some electricity, but only in the commissary, cookhouse and bunkhouses. Previous to that time, I remember battery radios only, and even those were scarce. My dad had one of the first battery radios in camp. For the benefit of others, he would place it in the kitchen window, and many of the employees would sit on the tracks next to the house to listen to heavyweight boxing. I remember the outcome of the fights, almost a contest between employees, when Dempsey, Tunney and others had a match. The company had a telephone system which connected the company store, cookhouse, railroad and Clatskanie office. Much of my dad's work involved calls concerning daily operation, machinery parts and other problems. The storekeeper was a medic and would alert the doctor in Clatskanie when a serious injury took place.

LIVING IN CAMP

Rudy Larson (boy in center) with his dog, his mother, aunt and father, Albin at Page Creek Camp of Benson Timber Company. What was it like living in a two-room railroad dwelling? There were good days, and there were bad days, Rudy reports. The fishing was good, but a runaway load of logs once knocked the steps off this dwelling. That was one day Rudy would like to forget. This photograph and the one below are from the Rudy Larson collection of Benson Timber Company near Clatskanie, Oregon. The photograph below is by Clark Kinsey.

Miscellaneous Related Steam Equipment

Above   An unidentified early experimental electric-powered yarder, converted from a steam donkey. Several large operators gave electric logging a try over the years. A few of the most notable were: the Sugar Pine Lumber Co. of Fresno, Calif., Potlatch Lumber Co. of Potlatch, Idaho and Long-Bell Lumber Co., Ryderwood Division, near Longview, Washington. Willamette Iron & Steel Works was a pioneer in this field.   *Oregon Historical Society, W.I.S.Co. Collection, OrHi 92934*

Left   A homemade donkey at the Collier Logging Museum, near Chiloquin, Oregon. *Author's photo, 1977*

In Search of Steam Donkeys

This may have been the first donkey assembled in Tillamook, Oregon. This photograph is from the Lee Johnson collection, but the Tillamook Pioneer Museum has a similar photograph of the engine with the following information: "Built by Birch Alderman and Andrew Anderson. Used to build right-of-way for Southern Pacific from Hobsonville to Tillamook." Date unknown.

Left and middle These donkey parts are in a field in Southern Oregon, just past a "No Trespassing" sign. I do not know if any of these parts go together, but I do know that going past that sign means trouble (one of the hazards of being a donkey freak). This was once a Washington wide face 12 x 12, frame No. 1683. There are four drums there, plus a Washington Iron Works friction device. *Author's photos, 1977*

Left Another example of what can sometimes be found. These are Willamette 9x11 cylinders and hoist, old style. *Photo by John Cummings at Glendale Oregon, 1964*

In Search of Steam Donkeys

Above   In 1919, Willamette Iron & Steel Works introduced their car-mounted units. This arrangement shown consisted of a four-drum 12 x 14 two-speed compound-geared yarder and a three-drum 9-1/4 x 10 duplex loader, powered by a single boiler, mounted onto one of the skidder cars (#a-27) built by Pacific Car & Foundry. This unit is factory number 13, which is one of two sold to Booth-Kelly Lumber Company of Wendling, Oregon in 1920. As can be seen, this factory photo was taken before a house was installed, and appears to be shortly after delivery.   *W.I.S.Co. photograph from Steven R. Gatke Collection*

Above A Willamette-built car-mounted "unit" skidder at an unidentified location. The loader in front is a duplex type. In later years, Willamette provided steel houses for their units. This house appears to be site-built. Note the "jill-poke" frame members in front, tight against the base of the spar tree to hold the unit in place. Also, the frame is blocked up, removing the load from the railroad trucks, thereby stabilizing the unit. *Oregon Historical Society, W.I.S.Co. Collection, OrHi92938*

Opposite A Willamette Iron & Steel Works factory photo of a car-mounted unit. This 1920 view shows a 12x14 2-speed compound geared yarder and 9-1/4x10 duplex loader (W.I.S.Co. unit No. 12), destined for Kerry Timber Company, near Kerry, Oregon. Duplex loaders can be easily identified by their two sets of cylinders, one above the other. This arrangement allowed totally independent operation of each tong line, and quick engine reversing by use of steam directional control valves. The drum in front with the ratchet was for spotting cars. Duplex loaders were built by Willamette, Washington, Smith & Watson and a few others. Note the rectangular fuel/water tank. *W.I.S.Co. photograph from Martin E. Hansen Collection*

683

This is not a steam donkey, nor was the photograph taken in Oregon. This photograph is included because it shows how steam was gradually replaced with internal combustion engines, and because two of the men in the photograph are mentioned in the book. C.E. VanCise (fourth from the left) is mentioned on pages 154 and 155; Fritz Burkhard (sitting below in front) is mentioned on page 227. Fritz later became much in demand as a hook-tender, then woods boss, because of his ability to get logs. Although serious about his trade, he is also remembered as a waggish guy, who like many loggers, worked hard and played hard. He has since passed on.   Photograph by Darius Kinsey, Washington Pulp and Paper, Neah Bay, Washington.   *Courtesy of Dick and Vernona VanCise*

EARLY DAY SKIDDER

This Lidgerwood skidder was photographed by Darius Kinsey in 1910, before high-lead logging had come into its own. Albert S. Kerry purchased and operated the first skidder on the Pacific Coast (Northwest Lumber Company, Kerriston, Washington). Note the position of logging in a "V" or "bight," the high-lead blocks hung by chains and not near the guylines without tree plates, a practice discontinued later on.   *John Labbe collection*

Skidder Logging System

The diagram below and the carriage detail on the next page illustrate how a skidder system works. A skidder by definition needs four drums to yard with. Also required is a strawline drum. Some skidders had nine or more drums. Guyline drums were used when equipped with steel towers (in lieu of a tree) and additional utility drums were used to make changes, or for other reasons. Railcar mounting was normal when assembled as a "unit," meaning that more than one set of drums were used, some of which were used for loading. When equipped with a tower, skidders could weigh up to 312 tons. Willamette Iron & Steel Works alone manufactured 63 units. Some of those were assembled into units after leaving the factory. Some of those 63 units were powered by electricity. 66 rail mounted skidders were built by Washington Iron Works.

The term "skidder" and "unit" are nearly identical. A unit is a composite of more than one engine in which one engine is used as a loader, and at least one other engine in the unit is used for yarding. A skidder, on the other hand, is a yarding machine using a tight skyline with a carriage. In most cases, a slack pulling drum is also required. This means that five drums are required to log: (1) skyline, (2) skidding line, (3) receding (haulback), (4) slack-puller, (5) straw line. Many skidders were equipped with guyline drums also.

This simplified drawing is not intended to illustrate how to rig a skidder tree. Normally, this tree would be rigged for

In Search of Steam Donkeys

loading in addition to yarding. Two sets of guylines are required for this type of yarding. There would be three sets of guylines if also loading.

The inset shows a cross-section of one type of skidder carriage. Not all carriages had a third (lower) skyline sheave as shown. The slack puller was sometimes located outboard of the other sheaves.

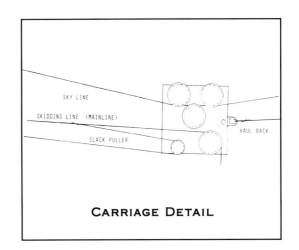

CARRIAGE DETAIL

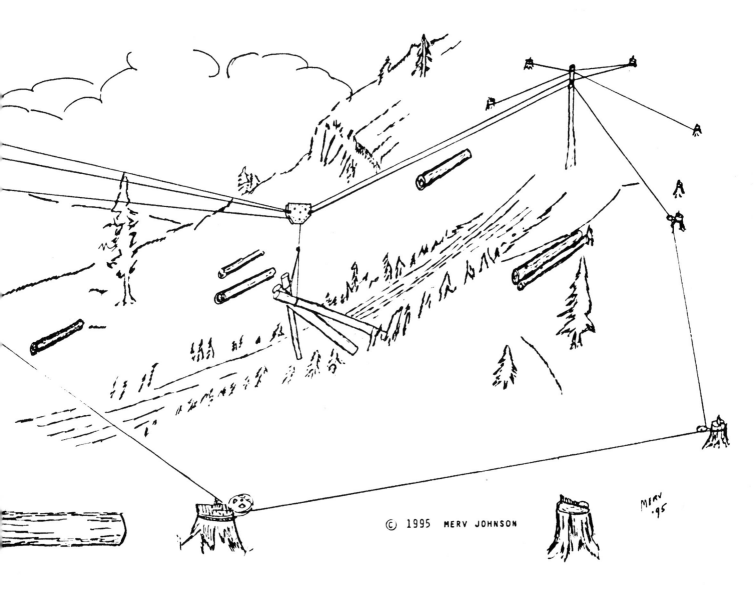

© 1995 MERV JOHNSON

SLACKER LOGGING SYSTEM

The slacker system (also referred to as "slack-skyline" by the manufacturers) used a carriage with a skyline that was lowered and raised for each turn of logs. It required four drums to log: one skyline drum, one skidding (mainline) drum, a receding (haulback) drum, and a straw line drum. It was not as complicated as the skidder systems, and did not require a slack-pulling drum. A tail-tree can be used, de-pending on the terrain. Slack is obtained by the weight of the carriage.

Even though the simple gravity-feed "shot gun" system (which uses only two drums for yarding) is very popular today, slacker-type yarders are still used because of the op-tions available with the additional yarding drum. However, they bear little resemblance to the steamers of yesteryear.

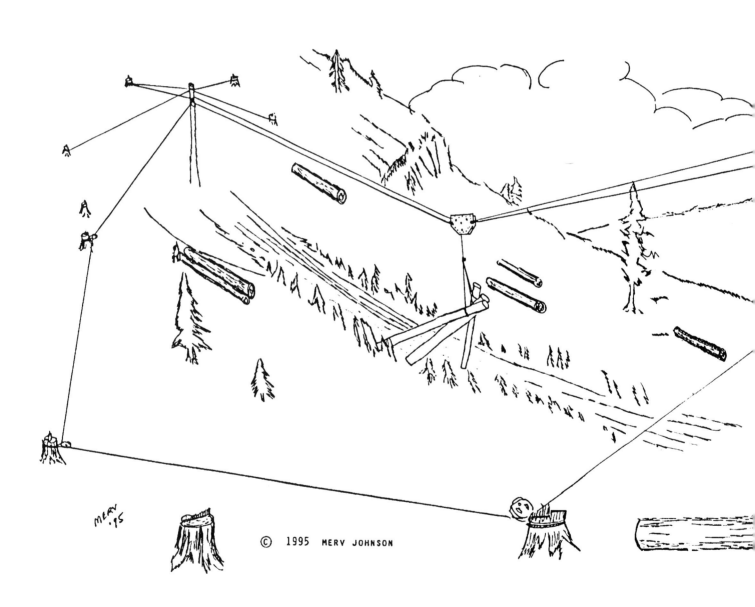

© 1995 MERV JOHNSON

In Search of Steam Donkeys

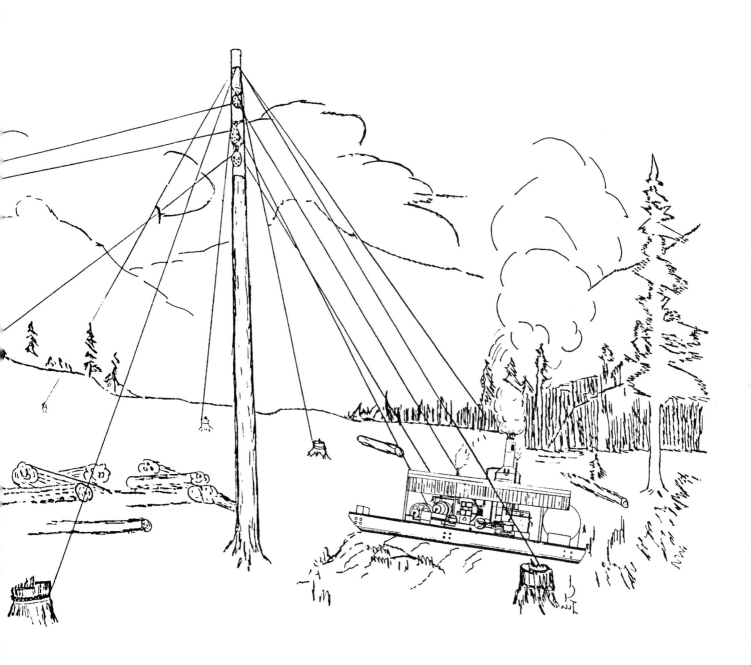

Above This view shows a Long-Bell Lumber Company Lidgerwood tower skidder, operating out of Vernonia, Oregon. This was one of the last steam logging operations in Oregon. *Courtesy of Alvin Elkins*

nfortunately, no remnants of the skidders used in Oregon are currently on display. Regardless, these giants should be mentioned here. According to an article in the October 1949 *Timberman*, upwards of one hundred Lidgerwood steel-spar skidders were in use on the Pacific Coast.

Unit skidders included loaders. Although Lidgerwood was the leading manufacturer of unit skidders and used the inter-locking-drum principle, Willamette Iron and Steel Works of Portland, Oregon also built a few such units. W.I.S.Co. built a tower skidder in 1927 for Crown-Willamette used at Cathlamet, Washington. This unit featured both a feedwater heater and a superheater (see page 230). It was a giant, unique machine with a one-of-a-kind tower. Not to be outdone, Washington Iron Works built a skidder equipped with feedwater heater and superheater in 1932, but with two additional features: roller bearings and an unusual interlocking engine.

The intricate rigging on these huge machines required capable people who sometimes specialized in this type of logging. "Skidder foreman" (sometimes "skidder rigger") was the term used to describe the boss, as opposed to "hooktender." Also, the term "leverman" was used as opposed to "donkey puncher." Although most high-lead steam logging systems utilized wooden spar trees, steel tower logging was not a new idea in logging history. The tower skidder machines originated in the South. The Pacific Coast version required large, bulky rigging, which in turn required large crews with plenty of muscle power. Generally confined to the railroad, they were efficient for shows which had a lot of timber. They could be used for both uphill as well as downhill logging.

In Search of Steam Donkeys

The same tower skidder in action, as on the previous page, showing a turn of logs about to be landed and a railroad car being loaded. This photograph was taken at the Camp Olson/Green Mountain operation. This was the last year of steam logging and railroading in the Vernonia area. *Photo by Ralph Swan, 1957*

Miscellaneous Related Steam Equipment

Left This unit skidder was photographed at Neah Bay, Washington. This was Crown-Willamette's unit skidder No. 2. It had a 120 foot tower. Average daily production was 125,000 board feet. *Darius Kinsey photograph from the C.E. VanCise Collection courtesy of Dick and Vernonia VanCise*

Opposite C.H. Wheeler Lumber Company operated this Willamette Iron & Steel Works tree-rigged unit skidder out of Cochran, Oregon. This was W.I.S.Co. unit No. 6, equipped with a 13 x 14 two-speed direct-geared yarder and a 9-1/4 x 10 three-drum duplex loader. *John T. Labbe Collection*

Above This was the 100-foot tower skidder built by Willamette Iron & Steel Works for Crown Willamette Company. This photograph was taken on March 11, 1927 at Cathlamet, Washington. *From the W.I.S.Co. Collection of Jack Taylor*

In Search of Steam Donkeys

Miscellaneous Related Steam Equipment

MOVING DAY FOR
CLARK & WILSON LUMBER COMPANY'S
LIDGERWOOD TOWER SKIDDER

These four photos show Clark & Wilson Lumber Co. moving their Lidgerwood tower skidder, about 1936. It took four locos to push it up the hill. These photographs were taken 3 to 4 miles east of Apiary Cutoff Junction, on Oak Ranch Creek Road, near Vernonia, Oregon. This skidder used a multi-sheave block to tighten the skyline. It could hold 3,000 feet of 1-1/8" skidding line, 5,500 feet of 1-1/8" haulback line, and a 2" skyline. They used 18 to 21 men to operate this machine. Some crew members in the photo below, shown right to left are: Ben Reinikka (chaser, later 2nd rigger (1); Chuck Wasser (2); Eddie Anlicker; Arnold Bay (whistle punk); Dwight Strong (6); Spurge Golden (7); Harold Tipton; Henry Wasser; Red Anderson; Harold Howard; Carl Halvorson (head hooker); George Pearl (fireman and/or watchman) (12); Not shown are: Oscar Vike (leverman); George Baker (on 2 spot Shay); Grant Layer (later became skidder foreman for about 11 years). The above names are from interviews with various Clark & Wilson employees. *Clark Kinsey photographs from Dwight and Judy Strong (below), others from Martin E. Hansen Collection*

In Search of Steam Donkeys

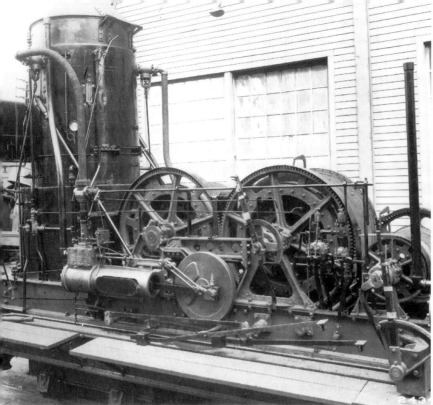

The interlocking device was an energy-saving option developed during the peak of steam logging. Patented by Lidgerwood for their skidders, the interlocking skidder has its skidding (main) drum "interlocked" through gearing to its receding line (haulback) drum, so that the receding line drum would feed line out as the skidding drum took it in, and vice-versa. This was a very desirable feature that helped to keep the rigging off the ground. Without interlocking, the only way to keep the rigging up was to apply the brake to the drum that was hauling out. When Lidgerwood's interlocking skidder patent expired in the early 1920s, the other major manufacturers rushed their own models onto the market.

This 12 x 14 interlocking unit skidder (model MTCL-SA25, unit No. 21) was turned out by Willamette Iron & Steel Works in March of 1923, a few years after Lidgerwood's patent on interlocking skidders had run out. It was sold to Big Creek Logging Company of Knappa, Oregon. The machine weighed-in at 172,740 pounds. *Willamette Iron & Steel factory photos from Martin E. Hansen Collection*

WHAT KIND OF MEN WERE THESE LOGGERS?

. . . Many are the times that Doc would dream of loggin'
in the glory days of steam.

The Willamettes and the Washingtons kept the riggin'
on   the go, but so did Doc-
'cause when he was hookin' he was a highball show-

and when he spotted the riggin' on a log,
the crew grabbed 'em hot in those days of the
"Frog."

But just the same, when the chokers were back,
they all loved to hear him yell for slack . . .

From "The Doctor of Loggin'" by the author

When I started in the woods in 1950, there were some "hardnosed" hooktenders still going strong. These men were the last vestiges of a philosophy that believed in a firm (or sometimes nasty) disposition on the part of a boss, who would drive the crew as hard as possible. Most of these men were amicable people "on the street," but as Fritz Burkhard was fond of saying, "When the starting whistle blows, all friendship stops."* The man who hired someone in the tavern the night before would take on a different personality the next morning. Although I remember one instance of the crew walking off the job in defiance of one hooktender who carried this sort of thing too far in 1951, crews were generally supportive of this philosophy and its work ethic, and insisted that their co-workers do their share.

Logger's nicknames were sometimes a clue to their personalities. For example, "Roughhouse" Dixon, and "White Hope" Anderson were named because of their experience in the ring. White Hope's reputation as a high climber was significant regardless of his fighting expertise. He reportedly demonstrated his physical prowess on the job by sailing his hat out of the spar tree, then attempt to beat it to the ground. There are numerous stories about this colorful character, most of them true. Another was "Jimmy the Monk," so named because of his agility as a climber.

Many crew members in the big camps retained their anonymity and were referred to as simply "Slim," "Blacky," "Whitey," etc. It was those who "paid their dues" by earning their reputations who eventually became known by more permanent names. High turnover in help was partly respon-

sible for the casual attitude toward the formality of learning names.

The heyday of steam logging was a time of high turnover, high wages, high-speed logging, high hopes, and high living. Many people were attracted to the woods because it was an easy place to get hired (and often fired), formal training was not required, and the wages were high. This favorable pay scale continued on through the early 50s. I remember a graduate mechanical engineer who elected to be a log scaler in the Kilchis Valley rather than endure the low entry-level salary of the engineering profession of the time. The logging woods attracted many capable people in its heyday. It took a good man—and a lot of time, effort and "jewelry" (rigging) to rig and manage a high-lead side.

Also, I remember loggers with missing arms or legs, which is uncommon today. Some of those men became whistle punks, others machine operators, and one I knew was a hooktender. I asked this last one why he chose logging as an occupation. After all, logging was probably one of the most difficult choices open to him. His answer was that he did not consider having only one arm a handicap! His one good arm was incredibly huge and his reputation seldom equaled.

I am willing to share names and experiences of the people with nicknames and handicaps mentioned (and more) on request. There were definitely a lot of colorful people when high turnover and big camps were common in logging.

Finley Hays, in his "Rigging Shack" column in *Logger's World* magazine, Feb. 1996, has provided a good insight of the mind of the logger. He states that it was the off-beat characters of the day that we remember, and like to talk about. Those who quietly went about their work and provided for their families didn't make good copy. His extended article is both entertaining and realistic.

Logging before the mid-1950s did tend to attract some off-beat characters. What kind of men were they, really? From being a logger myself, having a father who spent a lifetime as a logger and kept careful records, having other relatives as loggers, having close friends who are loggers, and as a result of conducting interviews and other logging research, I am prepared to generalize. Most loggers: (1) are hard, willing workers, (2) have little patience for those who are not, (3) are concerned about keeping things moving, (4) are people who enjoy their work (although some days it boggles the mind to imagine why anyone would want to be a logger), and (5) are people who like to talk about their work after hours (it has been said that more logging has been accomplished in the taverns than in the woods).

---

* Fritz Burkhard was a life-long logger. He died in 1988.

Miscellaneous Related Steam Equipment

Logger Life and Times

What kind of men were these loggers? Archie Samuel is the kind of character I generally think of when attempting to answer the question. Archie tried other occupations, but consistently ended up returning to logging. He worked his way through the ranks from whistle punk to contractor, with considerable time as woods boss along the way. Born in 1910, he started out as a whistle punk at age 15, and was a choker-setter by the time he was 17. I once asked him to relate any bad days he had in those fifty years in the woods. "None," he told me, "All were good."

Although he related his logging experiences fondly, his life had been far from serene. Following are some of his reflection on what life sometimes brought him:

Jail

When I was sixteen years old, a friend and I got hold of some moonshine. We proceeded to get drunk. The town constable and his helper, taking a dim view of this, attempted to take me to jail. I resisted, and got hit over the head several times with his sap. As I didn't have any money, I got ten days. One of my inmates, with scars from World War I (a veteran), was spending time waiting for the grand jury. His crime was stealing a dozen eggs. That kangaroo court was an experience.

The High-Ball Days

We landed in Seattle. We signed up through Archie McDougal's hiring hall for setting chokers at Washington Log on Hood Canal. We went from there to Crescent Log out of Port Angeles. They had good ground and old growth timber. They flew two 1 3/8" stiff-wire chokers. By keeping their yarding short, and trees rigged ahead with the lines out and blocks threaded, production was forty cars of logs per day. They had steel decked moving cars. It took one hour to move and start logging a new tree (this was before the steel towers of today).

Mud, Blood, Beer

I returned to Clark & Wilson Lumber Company where I could always get a job. As most of my friends, I drank pretty heavy on weekends. On one occasion, I got pretty well beat up. For a long time I didn't know who did it. I eventually found out. I became acquainted with him and asked how he had done it. Several times he passed it off, then on one occasion, at the dance at the Columbia County Fairgrounds, I acted as if I had more liquor than I actually had, upon which he decided to show me how he had whipped me. We flew at it. After some time, I delivered a hard right to the solar plexus which downed him. He laid there with his eyes open but couldn't move. This really scared me. Fortunately he recovered in a short time, after which we went to his house and drank some home brew. We have been friends ever since.

Hazards

We had a Greek powderman that we called Hemlock. He was a powerful man. His arms were the size of my legs. He would put a box of powder in his pack sack and head up a

Above Archie Samuel, at the memorial of Yunker & Wiecks Logging Company at Spruce Run. The school and the names of the teachers are recorded, along with that of Archie Samuel, Superintendent. Photo by Louis Buccini on Archie's 80th birthday, August 1990. Louis describes himself as a brother-in-law and best friend for over 60 years.

steep hillside without stopping. One time he was springing a hole to shoot a stump, The primer didn't go off. He started to dig it out a little too soon to allow for misfire. The primer went off in his face, which blinded him. He bellowed, "If I can't see I'll shoot myself." He was taken to the hospital and in a short time recovered his eyesight.

Humor

Back in the thirties, when I was woods foreman, we had old growth timber and hand fallers and buckers. I was out looking around in the woods and I heard two timber fallers up on springboards cussing each other. Concerned about this, I sneaked up closer. From where I was, it sounded like they were going to kill each other with their sharp falling axes. The head faller would say, "How much wood you got, you S.O.B.?" The second faller would respond in a like manner, and tell him how much wood was in the undercut. I made some inquiries and found out that they worked that way all the time. They were actually good friends.

(From Archie's book, *Oregon Logger, Life and Times of A.C. Samuel* by permission)

A party in honor of Archie's eightieth birthday was held at Spruce Run Park in the Coast Range in August of 1990. This had been the site of the Yunker & Wiecks Logging Company, where he was woods boss from 1937 to 1945. It was attended by relatives, friends, and past employees.

Archie died July 1, 1992.

How To Cross A Creek

Yes, steam donkeys have been known to overcome the obstacles of water by picking a good spot to cross, getting a good tailhold, and starting out with lots of steam to compensate for the probability of a quenched fire. These three photographs are a dramatic demonstration of logger and machine adaptabilty to such adverse situations. Location and date unknown. *Chris Horlyck Collection*

12 x 14 inch Humboldt Yarder about to ford a slough 160 feet wide, 8 feet deep. 150 pounds steam pressure.

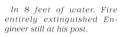

In 8 feet of water. Fire entirely extinguished Engineer still at his post.

Emerging on the opposite bank. Steam pressure 75 pounds

The above series of photographs comes from the 1925 Willamette Iron & Steel Works catalog, pg. 43. The view shows a 12 x 14 Humboldt yarder fording a slough at an unidentified location. *Courtesy of Glen Comstock*

RUNAWAY
DONKEY
WRECK!

Moving a donkey engine over steep or rugged terrain was a tricky operation. Occasionally, one would get away from its movers. This one, belonging to Big Creek Logging Company of Knappa, Oregon came to grief after tumbling down a hill. All the loggers could do was pick up the pieces and drag them back to the donkey doctor for repairs. The year was 1914.   *John T. Labbe Collection*

Miscellaneous Related Steam Equipment

This miniature donkey was built at the Willamette Iron & Steel Works around 1907. It was presented to Morton Insley, who was secretary and sales manager there. It later ended up at a Portland firm called "Loggers and Contractors." It was next donated to the Pacific Logging Congress, who in turn donated it to the old Forestry Building. When the building burned in 1964, the model was damaged beyond repair. *Photo from the Jack Taylor W.I.S.Co. Collection*

CHAPTER 8
MODELS & SCALE DRAWINGS

Modeling logging equipment got a late start. It would appear that there is more interest in modeling donkeys than ever before. Most of this modeling is done in HO and O scale, usually as part of a model railroad. Rare is a working model donkey and rigging. There were, however, loggers who constructed backyard working models for their kids. There also were children who put together crude working models of tin, wood, and other materials at hand. Unfortunately, few logging communities had homes with shops equipped with machines that could build sophisticated models, and it was hard to find more than one modeler in a given camp. Those few models completed were scrapped years ago, but a few exist under work benches, and tucked away on shelves. These modelers were generally unaware of each other, and there hasn't been much communication among them.

The first serious modeling that this author became aware of was done by Willamette Iron and Steel Works for their show room. Probably the next serious modeler was Rob Smith of Doty, Washington. According to his brother Paul, Rob built his first donkey model in 1932. Rob had no plans, which was the norm in those days. Factory drawings have now begun to surface, however, and there is much more information than ever before.

MODEL DONKEYS

. . . . . OR IS IT DONKEY MODELS?

As was implied earlier, the search for remaining steam donkeys has sometimes taken an unexpected turn. This chapter was to cover miniaturization, that is, donkey modeling. Well, somehow the interpretation took another path along the road in search of model donkeys. The photo above is certainly a donkey model, no doubt about that. Janice Johnson on this 9 x 10 Tacoma has a good grip on the main drum friction lever, but I don't know if 120 lbs. is enough to hold it down with a big log on the rigging.[*]

Left   As was common in the logging camps, there was at least one youngster attempting to "log" the backyard. There were no manufactured logging toys then. The toys that Santa brought to logging camps were often modified for logging, although crude, due to lack of tools and equipment. My father was donkey doctor at Consolidated Timber Co. at Glenwood, Oregon, and his smallest wrench was probably 7/16," but with a pair of pliers, hammer and tin snips, I managed to get a start. Little did I dream I would end up with the model yarder on page 250.   *Lee Johnson photo of the author, circa 1942*

[*]   According to Lee Johnson, there is a way to hold these levers down. When he worked for Joe Flora in about 1913 at Portland Lumber Company, he was having that very problem. Lee wasn't very heavy. Joe sized-up the situation with an alert eye of one who was destined for success in the timber industry. Without hesitation, he gathered up some large rocks. "Here Lee, put these in your pockets. They will hold you down."

3" SCALE LIVE STEAM

Rob Smith built these 3"=1' scale donkeys; a slacker, left, and a duplex loader, below. The models are now owned by Rob's brother, Paul, following Rob's demise.

Above   Rob Smith built this beautiful 3" slacker model.   *Author's photo, 1995*

Right   That's Paul running his duplex rigged to a heel-boom.   *Author's photo, 1995*

Below   Paul Smith running his 3" scale slacker. *Steven Gatke photo, 1992*

Below   Bob Sorenson at the controls of Paul's duplex loader. *Steven Gatke photo, 1992*

These photos show a Dolbeer vertical spool donkey in 1-1/2″ scale. This is a superdetailed work built by a professional modeler. This non-operating model is accurate down to the bolt heads. Scale reproductions are available from Bill Hudson of Eugene, Oregon. For address, see back of this book.   *Photos by Cliff Coles*

In Search of Steam Donkeys

Above   An HO scale Lidgerwood tower skidder built by Lyle Noah of North Plains, Oregon.   *Author's photo*

Below   An award-winning 1/4"=1' scale Willamette 12 x 14 Humboldt yarder, built by Philip Schnell.   *Photo by Katie Schnell*

THE MODELS OF LYLE SPEARS

During the late 1950s and early 1960s, Lyle Spears of Vancouver, Washington was busy documenting existing prototype logging equipment and scratch-building exquisite HO scale logging models. At this time, very few model railroaders were attempting to build highly detailed models of steam donkeys. Except for some brass locomotives, virtually nothing was commercially available for logging modelers, so extensive scratch building was the only way to have the models Lyle wanted (unfortunately, except in a few notable instances, this is still largely the case). Lyle wrote several articles for *Model Railroader* and *Railroad Model Craftsman* magazines that inspired many modelers to get started in logging. The realism of his models and photographs is stunning, especially when one considers the era in which they were made.   *All photos by Lyle Spears*

Top   This is really a model! Lyle's astonishingly realistic Western Logging Co. Camp.
Below left   Lyle's nearly completed Lidgerwood tower skidder.
Below right   A small wide face yarder with a drag bucket, a large incline engine, and a "cherry picker" in the rear.

 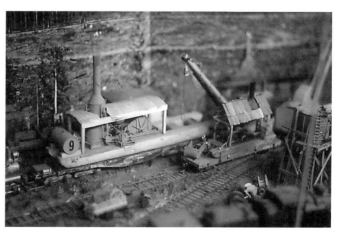

Top left   Lyle's Willamette 2-speed yarder.
Top right   Lyle's impressive car-mounted Willamette yarder & loader "unit."
Above left   A donkey on a moving car and a speeder make a trip across a log bridge.
Above right   The dramatic result of letting a boiler's water level get too low!
Below   The "unit" and the incline engine at Lyle's Western Logging Co. headquarters camp.

The models on these two pages show the diligent craftsmanship of Chris Horlyck of Carlton, Oregon. Chris has utilized the tools of his trade as a logging mechanic and machine operator to build a miniature yarding, loading and railroad logging system. So far, most of his equipment is patterned after Willamette Iron & Steel Works products. Chris appears in the photograph to the left. This photograph, and the one below, show his Humboldt yarder. The water/fuel tank on it reads: "Benson Timber Company." The bull block and other rigging are lying on the sled as was often done. Notice the Willamette emblem on the valve gear cover guard and the lettering cast into the front frame cross-member. Detail includes other items such as the supply pipe shut-off extension (valve handle showing in lower photograph) and a strawline drum that is equipped with a ratchet and a fairlead that feeds through the head block, and a spark arrestor. This donkey is operating on compressed air for the time being. In the photograph on the facing page, Justin Horlyck is landing a turn of logs. I suspect he is the youngest steam donkey engineer of all time! Yarding is accomplished via the North Bend system, complete with a fall block, cast tree plates, and a carriage dog to hold the carriage from running down the skyline when the logs are being unhooked at the landing.   *All photos by the author, 1983*

In Search of Steam Donkeys

Left   How many kids have an operating steam logging system in their backyard?

Right   This is a donkey book, of course, but how could one resist showing this model Willamette geared engine? Pride of workmanship is evident with the attention to detail, such as compound air pump and Willamette and Flora Logging Company lettering. Chris has this one powered by a shaft drive via a gas engine/hydraulic motor in the car behind the tender

Left   Model logging system built by Bill Edmondson on display in Butte Falls, Oregon museum. Bill, who has since passed on, was a retired logger who also built an operating steam boat. *Author's photo, 1977*

1-1/2" SCALE WILLAMETTE
TWO-SPEED YARDER

This model donkey, currently owned by the author, was built by Bill McCready of Milwaukie, Oregon, in the mid 1970s. The model was built using three photographs plus the details he remembered from the time he had spent as a donkey mechanic. Built to 1-1/2"=1 foot scale (1/8 size), it represents 12" bore by 14" stroke. Air controls represent the latest steam donkey technology. Out of view under the machine are three graduated air "jam" controls made from

This model is usually rigged in the "North Bend" system, in which the butt-rigging and chokers are attached to a fall block tail-holded into a carriage on a skyline. A head tree (spar tree) normally requires ten guylines. (Sometimes a "tail tree," using three guylines, was needed, too). The head trees were frequently between 160 and 190 feet tall (the head tree pictured is 20 feet high). The North Bend system was used primarily for cold-decking and "swinging" logs (a swing moves logs from one place to another, as opposed to yarding).

This is not a swing tree. While the North Bend system works best for modeling purposes—a completely accurate emulation of real logging practices is not always possible. However, authentic signals are used. See appendix for a list of signals. The duties of the crew members on the scale model operation are the same as those listed in the glossary. Those few people who model in this scale know that it takes a team of at least five people to operate such models properly. Standing up a 20-foot spar tree is definitely a group effort. The operation works best with a full crew—and it also produces a better show!

used truck-trailer brakes. Each drum has one lever. The day this picture was taken, the yarder was operated entirely by compressed air. When running on steam, a steam/air pump (not shown) allows self-sufficient operation. The sled is eight feet long.

The prototype Willamette Iron and Steel Works yarder, built in Portland, was developed during the heyday of steam logging, and was popular with the loggers. (Unfortunately, very few "W.I.S.Co." two-speeds are left; there is only one in Oregon, located at the Camp 18 Logging Museum in Elsie). The originals were fueled by crude oil, wood, or coal.

These photographs were taken in the woods near Coos Bay, Oregon, in the fall of 1995, at a recently logged site. The landing provided us with some stumps on which to anchor the guylines and the skyline. Where there were no available stumps, pipes were driven into the ground to act as anchors. When running this show in city parks, there are usually no stumps, so the anchoring is done on telephone poles, living trees, buildings, or, again, on pipes. (Today's loggers sometimes have problems finding stumps. Timbered areas are being logged for the second or third time, and many stumps are either rotten or not large enough to use.)

All photos on these two pages by the author, except below, by Peter Croyle

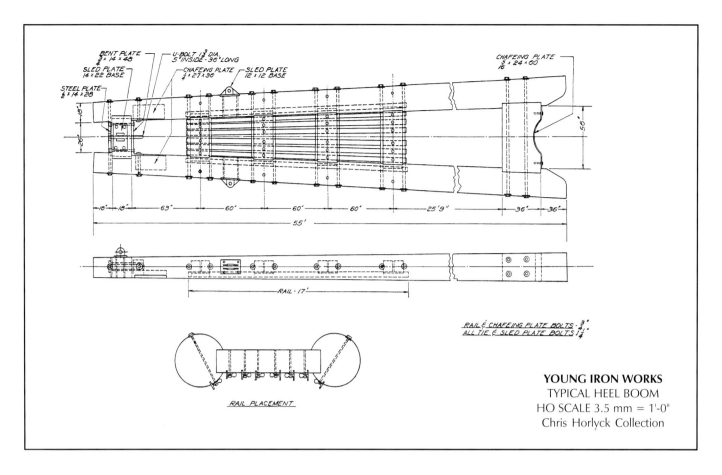

BENT PLATE
¾ x 14 x 48
SLED PLATE
14 x 22 BASE
U-BOLT 1¾ DIA.
5"INSIDE - 36"LONG
CHAFEING PLATE
¼ x 27 x 36
SLED PLATE
12 x 12 BASE
CHAFEING PLATE
⅜ x 24 x 60
STEEL PLATE
½ x 14 x 28

56'

18"   18"   63"   60"   60"   60"   25'9"   36"   36"

55'

RAIL - 17'

RAIL & CHAFEING PLATE BOLTS - ¾"
ALL TIE & SLED PLATE BOLTS 1¼"

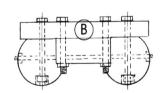

RAIL PLACEMENT

YOUNG IRON WORKS
TYPICAL HEEL BOOM
HO SCALE 3.5 mm = 1'-0"
Chris Horlyck Collection

The drawing below shows the cross-section and hardware involved in the construction of a typical heel boom. This design will also work for hayrack booms.

T-BAR OR
2 ANGLES

Ⓒ DRILL HOLES

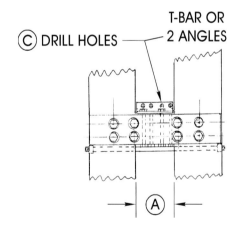

Ⓐ

Ⓐ NOT DRAWN TO SCALE. THIS
DISTANCE MUCH GREATER ON
HAYRACK BOOMS.

Ⓑ CROSS TIE WILL FIT ON TOP
OF PRESENT CROSS MEMBER.
IT SHOULD GO ALL THE WAY ACROSS.

Ⓒ T-BAR SHOULD BE ABOUT 1.5" THICK,
OR TWO .75" THICK ANGLES CAN BE
USED BACK-TO BACK.

Ⓑ

Ⓒ T-BAR OR 2 ANGLES   SHACKLE

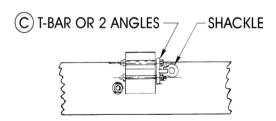

TYPICAL HEEL BOOM
HARDWARE DETAILS
NO SCALE
Drawn by Merv Johnson

The author's model heel boom in 1/8 size. The view on the right clearly shows the rails bolted to the underside to provide "grip" for healing up logs. This 8-foot long model represents a 64-foot long boom. I would like it longer, but it and my 8 foot long yarder sled need to fit on my trailer. *Author's photos*

MARSCHUTZ & CANTRELL "DOLBEER"
6 x 12 VERTICAL SPOOL DONKEY
(MACHINE #1)

HO SCALE: 3.5MM = 1 FOOT
DRAWN BY LYLE SPEARS (JUNE 1962)

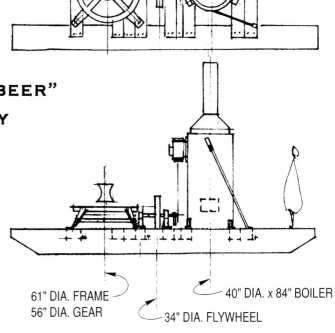

61" DIA. FRAME
56" DIA. GEAR

40" DIA. x 84" BOILER
34" DIA. FLYWHEEL

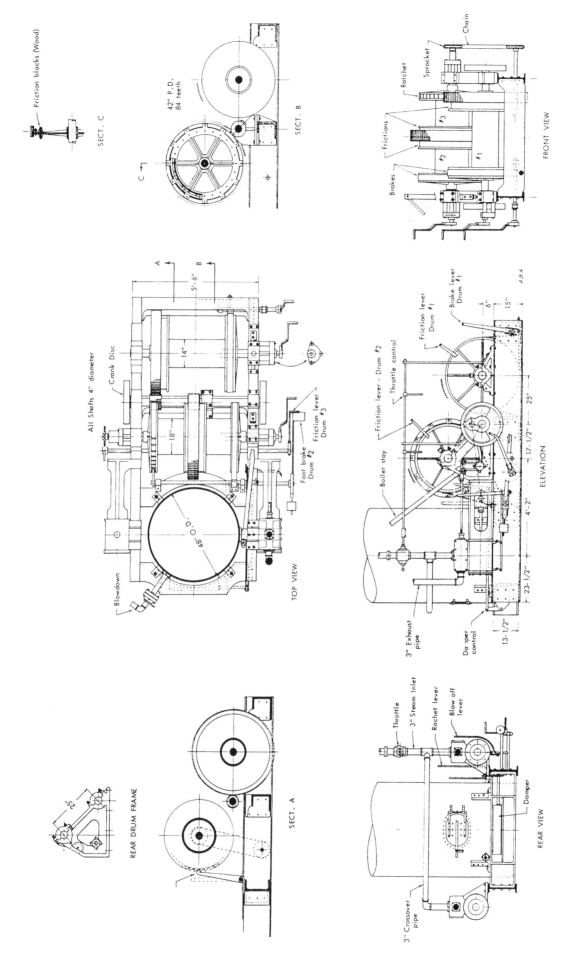

Friction blocks (Wood)

SECT. C

42" P.D.
84 teeth

SECT. B

Chain

Sprocket

Ratchet

Frictions

#3

#2   #1

Brakes

FRONT VIEW

All Shafts 4" diameter

Crank Disc

14"

18"

48" O.D.

Blowdown

Foot brake
Drum #2

Friction lever
Drum #3

A

B

5'-6"

TOP VIEW

Boiler stay

Friction lever - Drum #2

Throttle control

Friction lever
Drum #2

Friction lever
Drum #1

Brake lever
Drum #1

A B A

6"

15"

25"

17-1/2"

4'-2"

23-1/2"

13-1/2"

3" Exhaust
pipe

Damper
control

ELEVATION

REAR DRUM FRAME

SECT. A

Throttle

3" Steam Inlet

Ratchet lever

Blow off
lever

Damper

3" Crossover
pipe

REAR VIEW

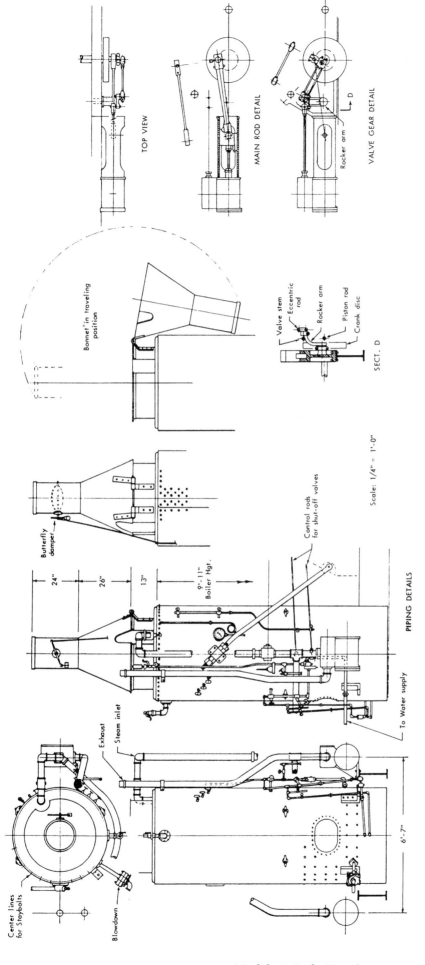

TOP VIEW

MAIN ROD DETAIL

VALVE GEAR DETAIL

Rocker arm

D

Bonnet* in traveling position

Valve stem

Eccentric rod

Rocker arm

Piston rod

Crank disc

SECT. D

Butterfly damper

Control rods for shut-off valves

24"

26"

13"

9'-11" Boiler Hgt.

PIPING DETAILS

To Water supply

Scale: 1/4" = 1'-0"

Exhaust

Steam inlet

6'-7"

Center lines for Staybolts

Blowdown

WILLAMETTE IRON & STEEL WORKS
9-1/4 x 10 LOADING ENGINE, CIRCA 1920

SCALE: 1/4 INCH = 1 FOOT

DRAWN BY ALAN B. ARMITAGE

REPRODUCED BY PERMISSION OF PRECISION SCALE COMPANY

* "Bonnet" is also referred to as "hood and stack" or "smokebox and stack."

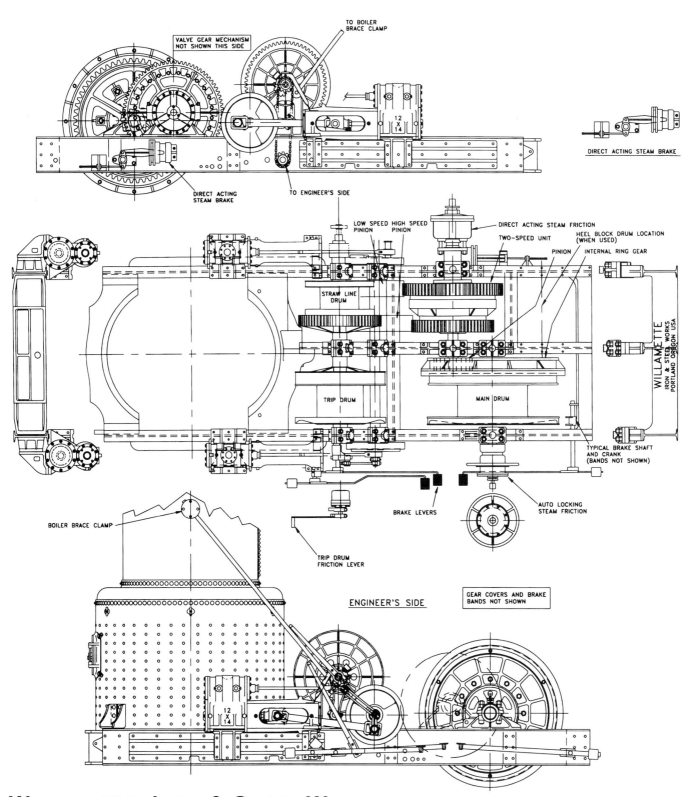

VALVE GEAR MECHANISM
NOT SHOWN THIS SIDE

TO BOILER
BRACE CLAMP

DIRECT ACTING
STEAM BRAKE

TO ENGINEER'S SIDE

DIRECT ACTING STEAM BRAKE

LOW SPEED HIGH SPEED
PINION   PINION

DIRECT ACTING STEAM FRICTION

HEEL BLOCK DRUM LOCATION
(WHEN USED)

TWO-SPEED UNIT

PINION   INTERNAL RING GEAR

STRAW LINE
DRUM

WILLAMETTE
IRON & STEEL WORKS
PORTLAND OREGON USA

TRIP DRUM

MAIN DRUM

TYPICAL BRAKE SHAFT
AND CRANK
(BANDS NOT SHOWN)

BRAKE LEVERS

AUTO LOCKING
STEAM FRICTION

BOILER BRACE CLAMP

TRIP DRUM
FRICTION LEVER

ENGINEER'S SIDE

GEAR COVERS AND BRAKE
BANDS NOT SHOWN

12
X
14

WILLAMETTE IRON & STEEL WORKS

12 x 14 COMPOUND-GEARED

2-SPEED YARDER, CIRCA 1925

(MACHINE No. 35, SHOWN WITH ORIGINAL BOILER)

SCALE: 1/4 INCH = 1 FOOT

DRAWN BY PHILIP SCHNELL

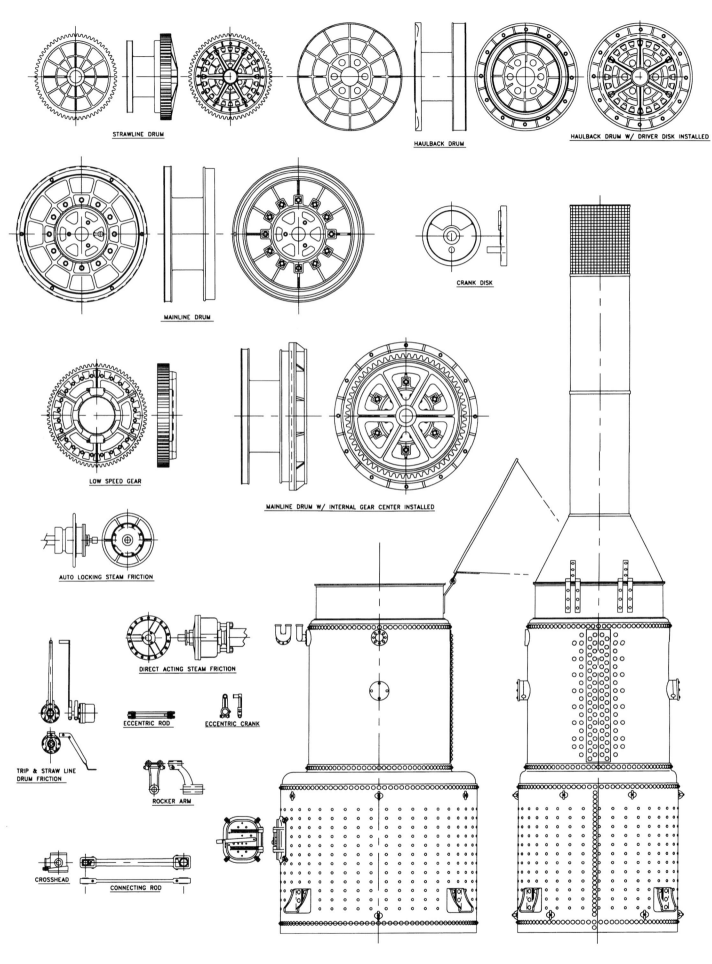

STRAWLINE DRUM

HAULBACK DRUM

HAULBACK DRUM W/ DRIVER DISK INSTALLED

MAINLINE DRUM

CRANK DISK

LOW SPEED GEAR

MAINLINE DRUM W/ INTERNAL GEAR CENTER INSTALLED

AUTO LOCKING STEAM FRICTION

DIRECT ACTING STEAM FRICTION

ECCENTRIC ROD

ECCENTRIC CRANK

TRIP & STRAW LINE DRUM FRICTION

ROCKER ARM

CROSSHEAD

CONNECTING ROD

Models & Scale Drawings

257

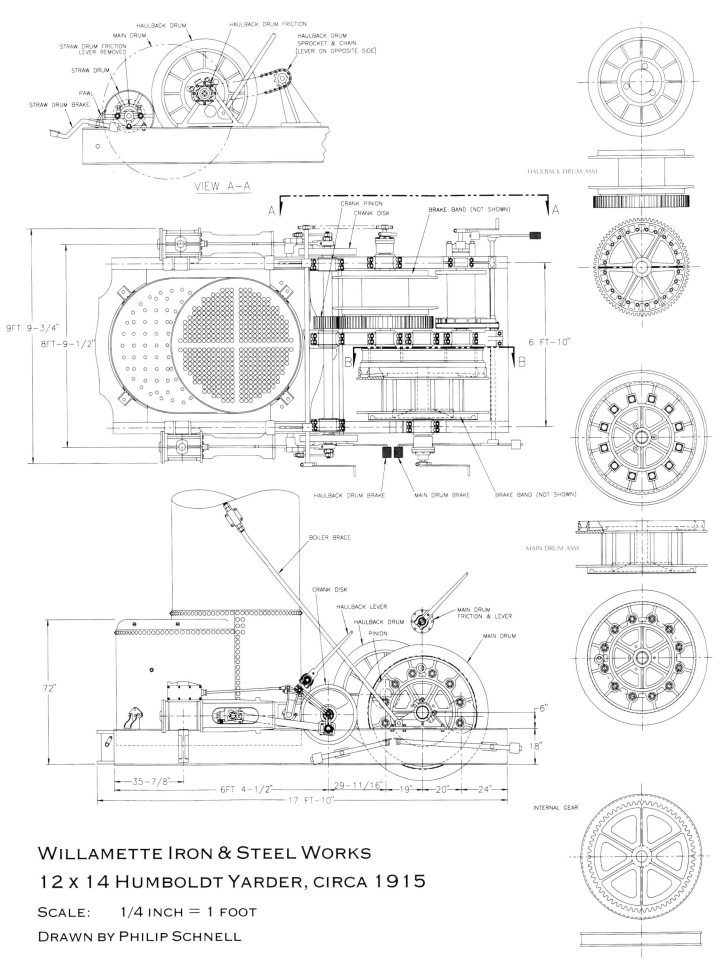

STRAW DRUM FRICTION
LEVER REMOVED

HAULBACK DRUM

MAIN DRUM

HAULBACK DRUM FRICTION

HAULBACK DRUM
SPROCKET & CHAIN
(LEVER ON OPPOSITE SIDE)

STRAW DRUM

PAWL

STRAW DRUM BRAKE

VIEW A–A

HAULBACK DRUM ASM

CRANK PINION

CRANK DISK

BRAKE BAND (NOT SHOWN)

A

A

9FT 9-3/4"

8FT-9-1/2"

B

B

6 FT–10"

HAULBACK DRUM BRAKE

MAIN DRUM BRAKE

BRAKE BAND (NOT SHOWN)

MAIN DRUM ASM

BOILER BRACE

CRANK DISK

HAULBACK LEVER

HAULBACK DRUM

PINION

MAIN DRUM
FRICTION & LEVER

MAIN DRUM

72"

6"

18"

35-7/8"

6FT 4-1/2"

29-11/16"

19"

20"

24"

17 FT–10"

INTERNAL GEAR

Willamette Iron & Steel Works

12 x 14 Humboldt Yarder, circa 1915

Scale: 1/4 inch = 1 foot

Drawn by Philip Schnell

In Search of Steam Donkeys

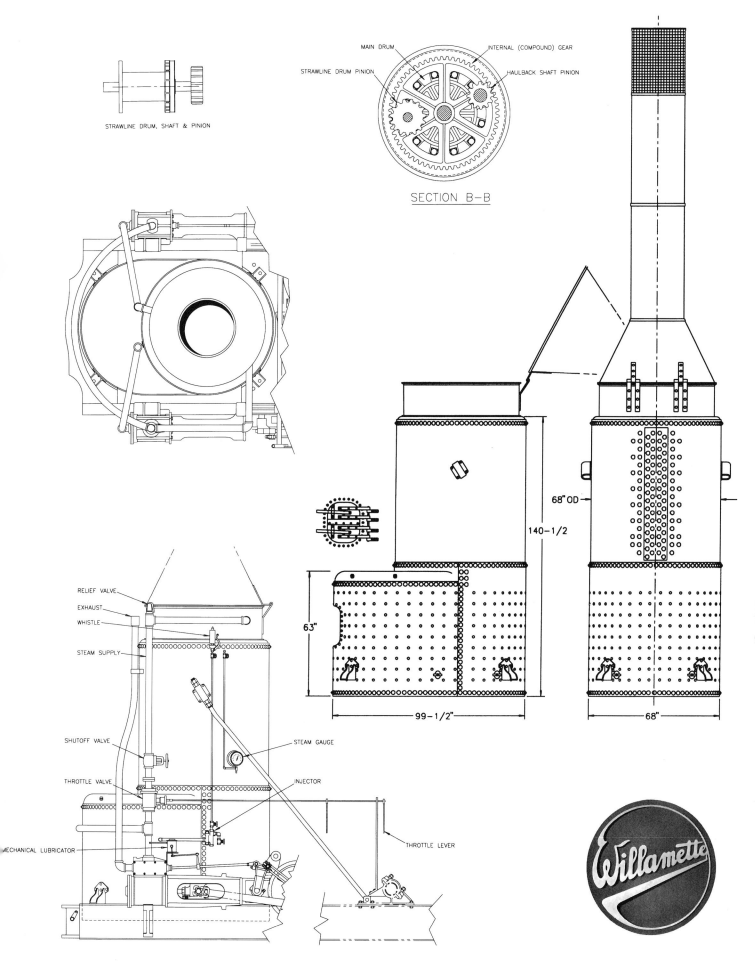

STRAWLINE DRUM, SHAFT & PINION

MAIN DRUM

INTERNAL (COMPOUND) GEAR

STRAWLINE DRUM PINION

HAULBACK SHAFT PINION

SECTION B—B

68" OD

140-1/2

63"

99-1/2"

68"

RELIEF VALVE

EXHAUST

WHISTLE

STEAM SUPPLY

SHUTOFF VALVE

THROTTLE VALVE

MECHANICAL LUBRICATOR

STEAM GAUGE

INJECTOR

THROTTLE LEVER

Models & Scale Drawings

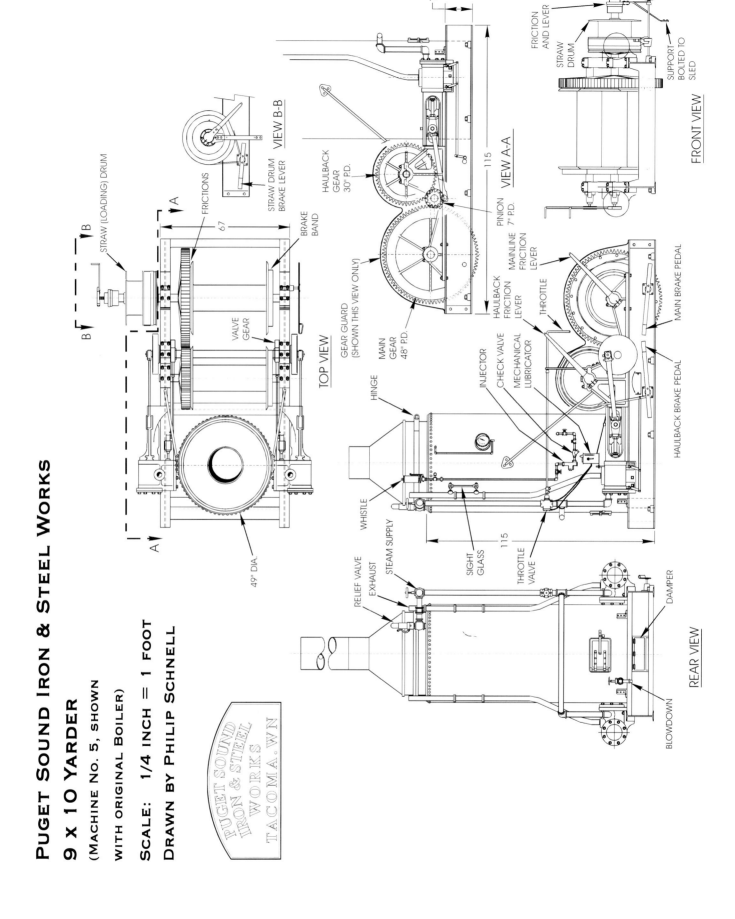

Puget Sound Iron & Steel Works

9 x 10 Yarder

(Machine No. 5, shown

with original boiler)

Scale: 1/4 inch = 1 foot

Drawn by Philip Schnell

PUGET SOUND
IRON & STEEL
WORKS
TACOMA. WN

STRAW (LOADING) DRUM

FRICTIONS

67

VALVE
GEAR

49" DIA.

BRAKE
BAND

STRAW DRUM
BRAKE LEVER

VIEW B-B

TOP VIEW

HAULBACK
GEAR
30" P.D.

GEAR GUARD
(SHOWN THIS VIEW ONLY)

MAIN
GEAR
48" P.D.

PINION
7" P.D.

VIEW A-A

115

HAULBACK
FRICTION
LEVER

MAINLINE
FRICTION
LEVER

HINGE

WHISTLE

STEAM SUPPLY

EXHAUST

RELIEF VALVE

INJECTOR

CHECK VALVE

MECHANICAL
LUBRICATOR

THROTTLE

SIGHT
GLASS

THROTTLE
VALVE

115

HAULBACK
FRICTION
LEVER

MAIN BRAKE PEDAL

HAULBACK BRAKE PEDAL

REAR VIEW

DAMPER

BLOWDOWN

15

FRICTION
AND LEVER

STRAW
DRUM

SUPPORT
BOLTED TO
SLED

FRONT VIEW

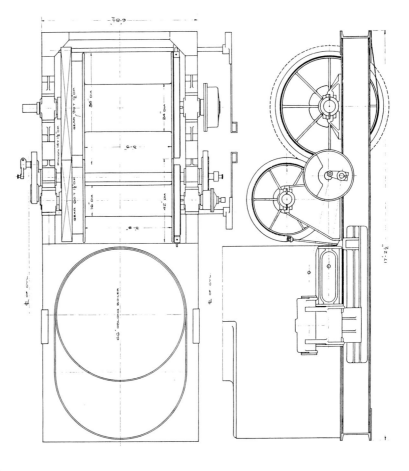

Washington Iron Works
12 x 14 Road Engine

Scale: 1/4 inch = 1 foot

Original Drawing dated 6 May 1918

Courtesy of Ken Schmelzer

Washington Iron Works
12x14 2-Speed Direct-Geared Yarder

SCALE: 1/4 INCH = 1 FOOT

ORIGINAL DRAWING DATED 7 JULY 1927

COURTESY OF KEN SCHMELZER

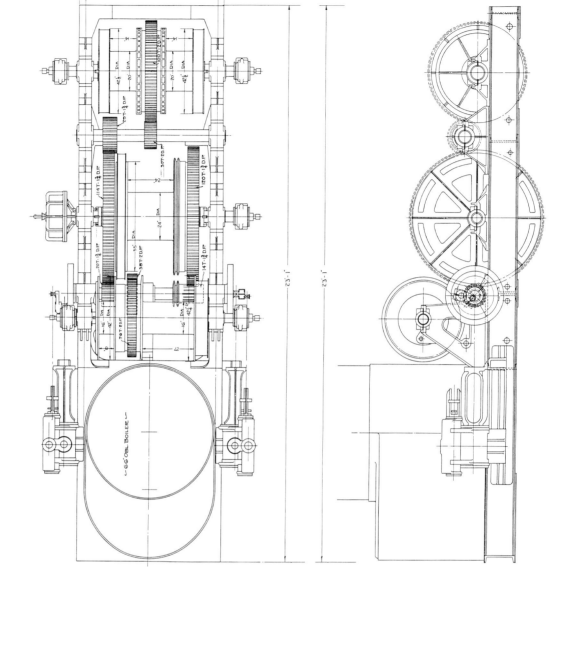

In Search of Steam Donkeys

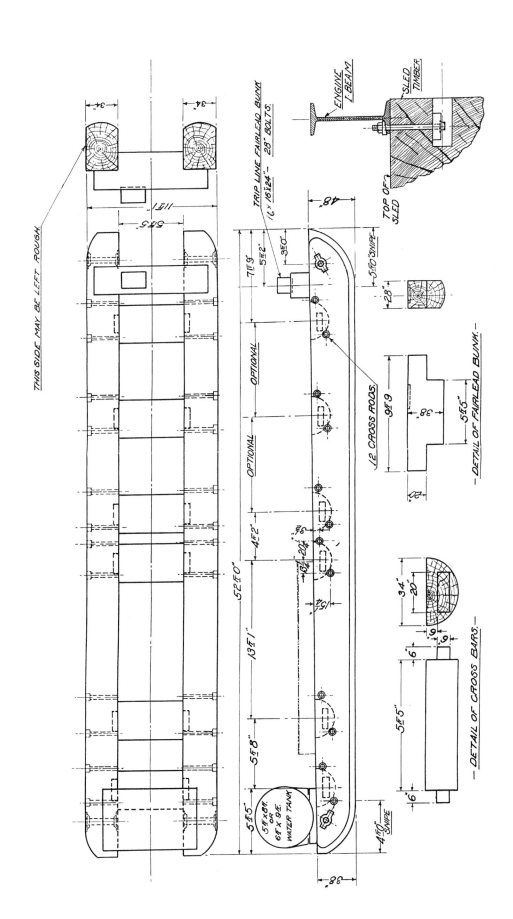

Willamette Iron & Steel Works

Donkey Sled Design for 11 x 13 Engines (1919)

Scale: HO (3.5 mm = 1 foot)

Silver Falls Timbr Co
C Kinsey Photo Seattle

APPENDIX

Above A scene repeated countless times in the Western Oregon woods; an unidentified Willamette wide face roader and crew pose for the camera. *Philip Schnell Collection*

Opposite The Silver Falls Timber Company operated out of Silverton, Oregon. A fairly large operation, they ran over 68 miles of railroad and had three geared and three rod locomotives. In this beautiful view, a small donkey, perhaps a loader, is being moved off of a moving car. *Clark Kinsey photograph, Martin E. Hansen Collection*

AUTHOR'S NOTES

Every attempt has been made to be as accurate as possible. However, there are some discrepancies between information in this book and in manufacturer's catalogs. This could be because of any of the following:

1. Modifications to equipment (often happens with loggers).
2. Catalog error.
3. Custom-built machines or options not listed in catalog.

4. Standard machine model or option not listed in catalog.
5. Tape measure error (mine).

Measurements in this book are approximate. As to historical accuracy, I welcome challenges to anything in this book and any additional information offered. Surely this will not be the last publication of this sort.

This unique early donkey had a submerged-head boiler. At right is Ira Withrow. Second from right is Roy C. Bell. This was at Skamokawa, on the Washington side of the Columbia River. *John T. Labbe Collection*

Left Moving a steam donkey across a creek. This was at the Mackey Place, about 1910, near where Detroit, Oregon is now located. *Oregon Historical Society ORHI 92106*

Other accounts of moving a steam donkey across a stream are found in:

Pages 237 and 238 of this book.

Logger's World - The First Ten Years, 1987, pg. 68, a story by Paul Reppeto reprinted from *The Way of the Logger*.

The Timberman, March, 1924, "Fording a River at Twenty-four Below" (on this one, the donkey fell through the ice, and they almost didn't make it).

ORGANIZATIONS IN OREGON WITH SIGNIFICANT
MATERIAL ON STEAM LOGGING

1	Collier State Park Logging Museum	US Hwy 97, 30 miles north of Klamath Falls, OR 97402	Prototype equipment
2	Lane County Museum	740 W 13th Ave., Eugene, OR	Some photos
3	Camp 18 Logging Museum	Elsie Rt. Box 195, Seaside, OR 97138 (Milepost 18, Hwy 26, Elsie)	Prototype equipment, some in operating condition, spar tree
4	Heritage Center Museum	1618 Exchange St., Astoria, OR 97103	One logging film plus other artifacts
5	Tillamook County Pioneer Museum	2106 2nd St., Tillamook, OR 97141	One operating donkey, photos, large new site planned
6	Douglas County Museum	PO Box 1550, Roseburg, OR 97470 (museum off I-5)	One donkey, photos
7	Oregon History Center	1230 SW Park St., Portland, OR 97205	The W.I.S.Co. collection, plans, photos, sales records
8	Umpqua Discovery Center	409 Riverfront Way, Reedsport, OR 97467	One donkey, video, photos
9	Columbia County Museum	511 E. Bridge St., Vernonia, OR 97064	Prototype equipment, photos
10	Coos-Curry Pioneer & Hist. Assoc. Musm.	Simpson Park (Rt. 101), North Bend, OR 97459	Photos, documents
11	Washington County Museum	17677 NW Springville Rd., Portland, OR 97229	Photos, documents

GLOSSARY

Bleeder Valve A valve in the supply pipe between the throttle and boiler with an exhaust extension. It allowed the engineer to lower items on compression by allowing the weight of the load to run the engines backwards without overcoming boiler pressure. It allowed better control than brakes (e.g. with a high climber in the spar tree.)

Bull Gear The largest gear on a donkey.

Butt Rigging The rigging connecting the choker(s) to the running lines, including the swivel.

Carriage A trolley which rode a cable. They were used as an aid in some types of high lead systems, the most common of which were the "skidder" and "slacker" systems.

Chaser Decides where to land logs and unhooks them as they are brought in by the yarder. Makes up strawline sections, takes care of rigging, makes changes needed on the landing when logging or changing roads.

Choker Setter The one who places chokers on logs, along with miscellaneous other duties. This is often referred to as the hardest and the lowest paid job.

Cold Deck A pile of logs.

Compound-geared A gearing system that utilizes more gears than a pinion and a driven gear.

Deck A pile of logs.

Direct-Geared See simple-geared

Donkey Doctor A donkey mechanic

Donkey Puncher An engineer, or one who operates a donkey.

Drum The reel that the cable is wound on.

Engineer As used in this book, one who operates a donkey.

Friction Device Also called a "jam." A clutch mechanism used to transmit power to the drum. Three types were commonly used: steam; compressed air; hand-operated.

Gypsy A horizontal spool on a donkey usually outboard of the main drum.

Haulback Drum Used to return rigging to the "brush." Originally called a "trip drum."

Head Block The large cross piece on the front of a donkey sled.

Head Loader Picks logs to be loaded and sets tongs; directs the second loader.

High Ball A fast-moving operation.

High Climber The one who rigs spar trees.

High-lead A system of logging in which logs are pulled and lifted partially or completely by rigging overhead.

Hooktender In charge of a side and crew, and how the rigging is accomplished.

Humboldt Yarder A type of compound geared yarder built by Willamette Iron & Steel Works.

Incline A logging railroad too steep for locomotives, the grade in which cars are pulled up and lowered by means of a cable.

Interlocked See page 234.

Knee-operated Boom Swing A lever that could be operated by the engineer's leg that moved the boom to left or right on some McGifferts and other loaders with attached booms.

Lagging 1. Asbestos insulation around the boiler, covered with a sheet metal jacket. 2. Wood placed on a drum core to increase diameter and, thereby speed on the rigging. 3. Wood strips used as a substitute for brake lining.

Main Drum Used to bring logs in or up.

Molly Hogan (or "Molly)	A small loop of cable made by winding a strand of cable around itself. These were used in the hole of a pin as a retainer, or sometimes used to hold strawline sections together, or for a number of other uses, such as a lifting handle.
Parbuckle	A cable passed around a log, causing it to roll. A common method of loading before highlead became common.
Receding Line	The haulback line that returns the carriage on a skyline show.
Rigging Slinger	Second in command under the hooktender. Picks out each turn of logs and gives vocal signals to the whistle punk. Makes skidroad changes. Directs the choker-setters
Road Donkey	Sometimes called a "roader." The name dates these machines to pre-high-lead days in many cases. They were swing donkeys with large drums.
Sail Guy	The cable used to hold up a loading boom.
Second Loader	Spots trucks or railroad cars, unhooks tongs, shifts logs if necessary, and brands logs.
Show	A logging operation.
Simple-geared	Gearing system using only one pinion and a driven gear. Same as "direct-geared."
Skidder	A donkey used on a system that utilized a standing skyline and a carriage with a slack-puller.
Spar Tree	A wooden or steel tower with rigging used in highlead systems to provide lift when handling logs.
Skyline	A large cable, used in skyline or slackline logging upon which the carriage travelled.
Spring Pole	A system of one or two small branches or vine maples which acted as a spring connecting the whistle wire to the whistle.
Spool-off Man	Logger who coiled the line as it came off the vertical spool of a Dolbeer donkey or gypsy.
Strawline Drum	Used to change road lines and other miscellaneous uses. Also called "haywire" drum.
Steam Supply Pipe	The pipe that carries dry steam (ideally) from boiler to cylinders.
Swing Donkey	A donkey used to move logs from one place to another, as opposed to yarding or loading.
Swing Road	The path where logs are moved from one place to another, as opposed to yarding or loading.
Tacoma	A name for the donkeys built by the Puget Sound Iron and Steel Works of Tacoma, Washington.
Tailhold	A place to anchor the end of a cable, usually a stump. There were several methods used. Walter McCulloch's book, *Woods Words* lists five definitions for this term.
Tight Skyline	Any skyline, such as a skidder, which leaves the skyline tight while logging. Also called "stiff-line."
Tommy Moore or "Tommy"	A pulley block with a wide sheave, especially one large enough to allow the butt-rigging to pass through.
Torpedo	A fuel tank that contains crude oil that could be dragged on the ground or otherwise transported on the rigging. Being pointed on one end, they resembled their underwater namesake.
Tree	A spar tree.
Trip Drum	Haulback drum.
Walking Anchor	The tail hold used on the head end of the skyline on a skidder show. Normally composed of two stumps, it was moved, or "walked," partially using existing stumps on each change, rather than changing to a completely new set of stumps each time.
Whistle Punk	A person who transmits signals from the yarding crew to the donkey. This job was phased out as radio whistling came in.
W.I.S.Co. or Willamette	Willamette Iron and Steel Company of Portland, Oregon. Manufacturer of steam engines and the Willamette geared locomotive.
W.I.W. or Washington	Washington Iron Works of Seattle, Washington. Manufacturer of steam engines, and later, diesel logging equipment.
Wood Buck	Wood cutter for wood-fired donkeys.
Yarder	A donkey used to bring logs to a landing.

WHISTLE SIGNALS

AUDIBLE SIGNALS, GENERAL

1 long	Stop water
1 long—1 short	Start or quitting
2 long	Water
2 long—3 short	Donkey doctor
3 medium	Hooktender (followed by 4 shorts, calls the crew)
3 long	Locomotive to switch side
3 long—2 short	Climber
4 long	Foreman
1 long—1 short repeated	Fire
7 long—2 short	Man hurt; locomotive and stretcher
6 long	Section crew
Group of shorts repeated	Runaway

AUDIBLE SIGNALS FOR SKIDDERS

1 short	Stops moving carriage. Stops or goes ahead on slack puller, as case may be, if carriage is stopped.
2 short	Go ahead on skidding line, holding carriage
1 short—2 short	Pick up skidding line, easy
2 short—1 short	Shake up carriage to clear choker
2 short—2 short	Ahead on receding line
3 short	Ahead on carriage, holding at present level, using interlock
3 short—3 short	Ahead easy on skidding line
2 short—2 short—2 short	Slack skyline, cable down
2 short—2 short—2 short—1 short	Pick up skyline, cable up
2 short—2 short—4 short	Slack receding line
2 short—4 short	Slack skidding line
2 short—2 short—1 short	Tighten all lines
1 short—4 short	Slack off slack puller
1 short—2 short	Pick up slack puller when slack
2 short—2 short—1 short or more	When carriage is in: to be used for number of chokers wanted
2 short—2 short—1 long	To be used for bull choker
1 short	When carriage is in: inspect butt rigging
2 short—4 short—1 short or more	For each additional ten feet of tong line
1 long—1 short or more counted	Number of coils of strawline wanted
5 medium	Tail or second rigger
5 medium—4 short	Tail or second rigger and his crew
2 medium	Skidder head rigger
3 medium—4 short	Hooker and his crew
2 long	Ahead on transfer
2 long—4 short	Slack transfer
1 short—3 short	Ahead on carriage with slack puller line
1 long	Ahead on strawline
1 long—4 short	Slack strawline
1 long—3 short	Ahead easy on strawline

AUDIBLE SIGNALS WHEN BUTT RIGGING IS AT THE TREE

1 short	Chaser inspect and repair rigging
1 short—then 2 short	Bull choker
2 short	No choker
2 short—then 1 short	One choker
2 short—then 2 short	Two chokers
2 short—4 short	Slack haul-back and hold all lines until 2 short is blown
3 short—1 short	Strawline back on haul-back

AUDIBLE SIGNALS FOR SLACK LINES

2 short—2 short—2 short—1 short	First cable up when road has been changed and tail hold made fast
2 short—2 short—2 short	Drop skyline
1 short	Stop any moving line
1 long	When logging, slack skyline
1 long—2 short	Ahead easy on skyline
2 short	Ahead on skyline
3 short	Ahead on skidding line, holding haulback
3 short—3 short	Ahead easy on skidding line with slack haulback
4 short	Slack skidding line
2 short—2 short—repeated once	Ahead easy on haulback with slack skidding line
2 short—2 short	Ahead on haulback
2 short—2 short—4 short	Slack haulback
2 short—pause—3 short	Pickup skyline and skid
2 short—pause—2 short—2 short	Pickup skyline and skin
3 short—1 short	When carriage is in: strawline back on haulback
3 short—1 short—2 short	When carriage is in: strawline back on carriage
3 short—2 short	Tight line
3 short—1 short—4 short	Slack strawline
3 short—1 short—3 short	Pull easy on strawline
2 long	Ahead on transfer
2 long—4 short	Slack transfer
2 long—2 short—2 short	When carriage is in: transfer back on carriage
1 long—1 short or more spaced	When carriage is in: number of coils
2 short—2 shorts—1 or more shorts spaced	When carriage is in: number of chokers
1 short	When carriage is in: inspect rigging repair and send back
2 short—2 short—4 short	When carriage is in: slack haulback and hold all lines until 1 short is blown, then send back
3 short—3 short	When carriage is in: send back powder
5 medium	Tail rigger
5 medium—4 short	Tail rigger and his crew
3 medium	Head hooker
3 medium—4 short	Second hooker and his crew

(See illustrations for hand signals—pages 132 to 137.)

AUDIBLE SIGNALS FOR HIGH LEAD

1 short	When all lines are stopped; ahead on main-line
1 short	When any line is moving; stop
2 short	Ahead on haul-back
2 short—1 short	Slack haul-back
2 short—then 2 short	Ahead on haul-back—slow
3 short	Ahead on mainline—slow
3 short—1 short	Ahead on strawline
3 short—1 short—2 short	Strawline back on rigging
3 short—1 short—3 short	Ahead on strawline—slow
3 short—1 short—4 short	Slack strawline
3 short—2 short	Tight line
3 medium	Hooker
3 medium—4 short	Hooker and his crew
4 short	Slack mainline

Safety Code for Logging, Oregon State Industrial Accident Commission, May 15, 1958

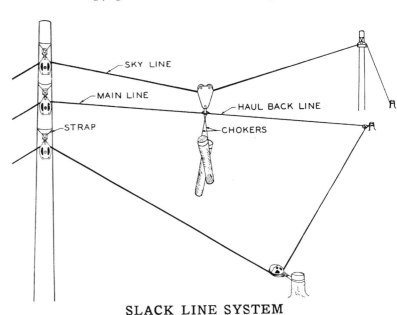

ADDITIONAL RIGGING DIAGRAMS

The diagrams on pages 271 through 273 are taken from a Broderick & Bascom wire rope catalog of 1939, from the Steven Gatke Collection. These diagrams are similar to others published by the several other leading wire rope manufacturers of the steam era. This may be the most controversial part of this book. Your author and the publishers debated at length whether to include all of these diagrams. These are not intended to be taken per-se as to how rigging was done, but they do present the basic idea without clutter. Loggers will take exception to some of the terminology and other details. One reason for doing this book is to clear up some bad information that has been perpetuated. There are drawings elsewhere in this book that are more authentic in their representation of the various systems. It is hoped that some of these drawings on the following pages will stimulate further study and discussion.

MAIN LINE

STRAP

HAUL BACK LINE

HIGH LEAD SYSTEM

Notes: High-lead blocks should *not* be hung with an extra wrap around the tree as shown. The extra wrap caused the strap to dig into the tree.

SKY LINE

MAIN LINE

STRAP

HAUL BACK LINE

CHOKERS

SLACK LINE SYSTEM

SKY LINE

MAIN LINE

STRAP

CHOKERS

HAUL BACK LINE

NORTH BEND OR TIGHT SKYLINE SYSTEM
(Single Part Main Line)

ADDITIONAL
RIGGING
DIAGRAMS,
CONTINUED

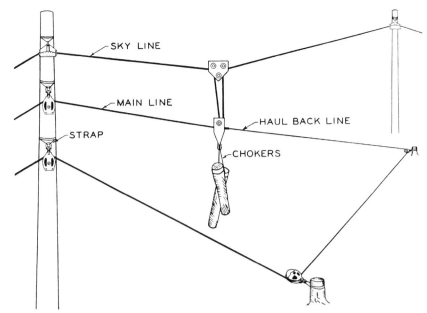

SKY LINE

MAIN LINE

HAUL BACK LINE

STRAP

CHOKERS

Right   Author's name for this system would be South Bend or Two-part North Bend System.

NORTH BEND (Two Part Line) or
TIGHT SKYLINE SYSTEM (Block Purchase)

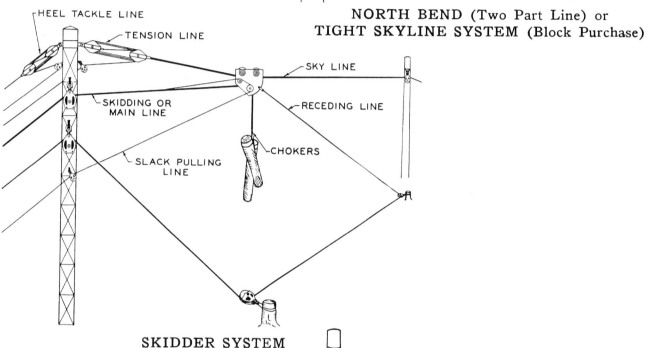

HEEL TACKLE LINE

TENSION LINE

SKY LINE

SKIDDING OR MAIN LINE

RECEDING LINE

CHOKERS

SLACK PULLING LINE

SKIDDER SYSTEM

Right   More commonly called the "Tyler" system.

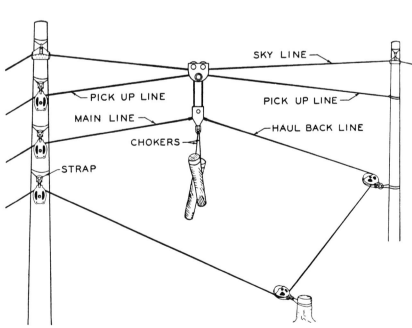

SKY LINE

PICK UP LINE

PICK UP LINE

MAIN LINE

HAUL BACK LINE

CHOKERS

STRAP

SUSPENSION CARRIAGE SYSTEM

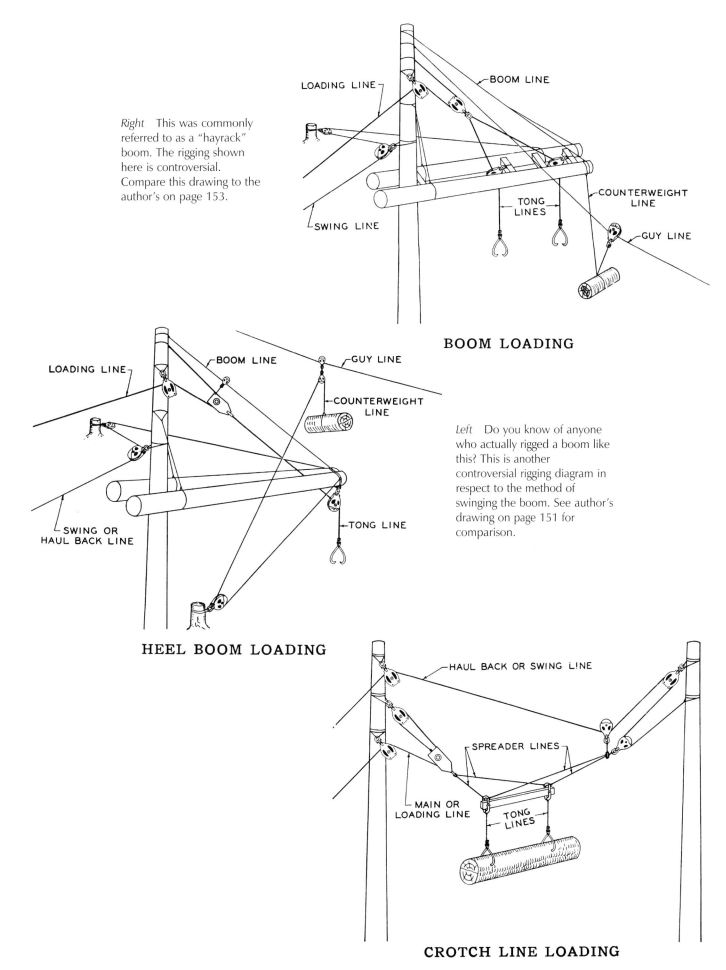

Right This was commonly referred to as a "hayrack" boom. The rigging shown here is controversial. Compare this drawing to the author's on page 153.

LOADING LINE

BOOM LINE

SWING LINE

TONG LINES

COUNTERWEIGHT LINE

GUY LINE

BOOM LOADING

LOADING LINE

BOOM LINE

GUY LINE

COUNTERWEIGHT LINE

SWING OR HAUL BACK LINE

TONG LINE

HEEL BOOM LOADING

Left Do you know of anyone who actually rigged a boom like this? This is another controversial rigging diagram in respect to the method of swinging the boom. See author's drawing on page 151 for comparison.

HAUL BACK OR SWING LINE

SPREADER LINES

MAIN OR LOADING LINE

TONG LINES

CROTCH LINE LOADING

WANT MORE INFORMATION?

Additional dimensions, photos, and background information are available for most equipment in this book.

Locations of some donkeys are unlisted because of any combination of the following reasons:

1.   Owners want it that way.

2.   Theft and vandalism.

3.   Owners prefer serious requests only.

4.   Some cannot be found without explicit instructions and backcountry travel.

If you wish to contact the author, your inquiry will be forwarded. Send inquiries to Merv Johnson c/o the publisher, TimberTimes, P.O. Box 219 Hillsboro, OR 97123. Or, visit my web site at: www.spiritone.com/~camp2/index.html

Thank you,

Merv Johnson

Right   Willamette Iron & Steel Works built this hydraulically-controlled incline snubbing engine for an unidentified customer.   *Oregon Historical Society, W.I.S.Co. Collection, OrHi 92935*

SOME SUGGESTIONS FOR CONTINUED
STEAM DONKEY RESEARCH AND NEWS

Logger's World
4206 Jackson Highway
Chehalis, WA   89532
www.forestindustry.com/loggersworld/

Logging industry magazine, occasionally mentions steam. Published monthly.

Oso Publishing Co.
31328 N. Brooks Creek Rd.
Arlington, WA   98223
www.osorail.com

Publishes *Tall Timber Short Lines* (quarterly magazine) and books.

TimberTimes Publishing Co.
PO Box 219
Hillsboro, OR 97123
www.timbertimes.com

Publishes *TimberTimes* (quarterly magazine). TimberTimes also publishes books, including this one.

4L (Loyal Legion of Logged-on Loggers)
4L-owner@yahoogroups.com

An internet e-group dedicated to logging modeling and history.

Camp 2 web site
www.spiritone.com/~camp2/index.html

the author's internet web site dedicated to steam era logging history.

Taubeneck & Henderson
14314 N Dayton Ave. N
Seattle, WA 98133-6838

Information on donkeys constructed by Clyde Iron Works, Washington Iron Works, Willamette Iron & Steel Works, and minority builders.

BIBLIOGRAPHY

Books, atlas and directories

Abbey's Register. Portland, Oregon: The Industrial Service Co. 1922 and 1926.

Adams, Kramer. *Logging Railroads of the West*. Seattle Washington: Superior Publishing Co., 1961.

Allen, Alice Benson. *Simon Benson: Northwest Lumber King*. Portland, Oregon: Binfords and Mort, 1971

Austin, Ed and Dill, Tom. *The Southern Pacific in Oregon*. Edmonds, Washington: Pacific Fast mail, 1987.

Austin, Ed and Dill, Tom. *The Southern Pacific in Oregon Pictorial*. Edmonds, Washington, 1993.

Frantz, W.C. *Timber up the Lukiamute*. 1978.

Hauff, Steve and Gertz, Jim. *The Willamette Locomotive*. Portland, Oregon: Binford and Mort, 1977.

Hirsimaki, Eric. *Lima: The History*. Edmonds. Washington: Hundman Publishing, Inc., 1986

Koch, Michael. *The Shay Locomotive: Titan of the Timber*. Denver, Colorado: World Press Inc., 1971.

Labbe, John T. and Goe, Vernon, *Railroads in the Woods*. Berkeley, California: Howell-North, 1961.

McArthur, Lewis A. *Oregon Geographic Names*. Portland, Oregon: Oregon Historical Society, 1982.

McCulloch, Walter F. *Woods Words*. Portland, Oregon: Oregon Historical Society/Champoeg Press, 1958.

Museums and Sites of Historical Interest in Oregon. Portland, Oregon: 1980, Oregon Historical Society

Oregon Atlas & Gazetteer. Freeport, Maine: Delorme Mapping, 1991.

Palmer, Lloyd M. *Steam Towards the Sunset: The Railroads of Lincoln County*. Newport, Oregon: Lincoln County Historical Society, 1982.

Robertson, Donald B. *Encyclopedia of Western Railroad History: Vol. 3, Oregon and Washington*. Caldwell, Idaho: Caxton Printers, 1995.

Samuel, A.C. *Oregon Logger*. Bend, Oregon: Maverick Publications, 1991.

Tabor, Thomas T. III and Casler, Walter *Climax, an Unusual Steam Locomotive*. Morristown, New Jersey: Railroadians of America, 1960

Catalogs and Brochures

John Dolbeer Logging Engine, Patent #256,533. U.S. Patent Office, 1882.

Wire Rope Catalog. St. Louis, Missouri: Broderick & Bascom Rope Co. , 1939

Clyde Equipment Company. *Clyde Log Loaders*. Duluth, Minnesota, (no date).

Mallory Company. *Logging Equipment Catalog*. Portland, Oregon: 1921.

Moxley Oil Burning Equipment Company, Inc. *Moxley Oil Burning Equipment Catalog*. Hoquiam, Washington (no date).

Oregon Accident Prevention Division. *Logging Safety Code*: various years.

Pacific Spruce Corporation 1924 report (reproduction). Newport, Oregon: Lincoln County Historical Society (no date).

Smith and Watson Iron Works. *Logging Equipment Catalog #9*. Portland, Oregon (no date).

Willamette Iron and Steel Works. *Logging Machinery Catalogs*. Portland, Oregon: 1913, 1920, 1925.

Periodicals

Wysong, Jenelle W. "Locals Find Steam Donkey in Woods." *Vernonia Freedom*, 10 July 1980.

"Logging the Willamette Valley." *West Coast Lumberman*, January 1937.

"Old 'Steam Pot' Added to Garibaldi Collection." *Headlight Herald*, 21 August 1929, p.19.

The Timberman, Portland, Oregon: various issues.

"This Business of Loading Logs." *Loggers World*, May 1978, p. 8.

West Coast Lumberman. Seattle, Washington: various issues.

ACKNOWLEDGMENTS

I wish to thank all those who have helped me on this book. *In Search of Steam Donkeys* has been in the works for twenty years, and could not have been completed without the assistance of many friends and colleagues. My apologies to anyone I may have failed to recognize.

I have relied a great deal on the legacy of photographs and information left me by my father, Lee Johnson, who died in 1981. Lee started running steam donkeys in 1912. He followed the logging industry as either a yarder engineer or donkey doctor into the 1960s. His life and work were the inspiration for this book.

My thanks to those people who have contributed valuable technical information about the machinery used in old-time logging. John Cummings is a logging-oriented equipment buff, especially during the tail end of the steam era; logging railroad historian John T. Labbe provided many photographs and reviewed the manuscript of the book; Bill Hudson, a professional modeler, is a reliable resource for information on spool donkeys; Lyle Spears, a modeler of Willamette steam donkeys and related equipment, contributed a drawing of Machine No. 1, along with photographs of his models; Jack Taylor, a Willamette Iron and Steel Co. sales engineer, has preserved many of the original engineering drawings, records and photographs; Doug Warneke provided his Smith & Watson catalog and photographs; Ken Schmelzer contributed two Washington Iron Works erection drawings; Martin E. Hansen not only made his entire extensive photo collection available, but furnished invaluable layout suggestions and uncounted hours of editorial assistance; John Taubeneck, of *Tall Timber–Short Lines* magazine, has devoted himself to collecting any information on steam donkeys he can find—he and John Henderson have taken the time to amass all the steam donkey sales records they can locate (John is probably the first person to compile them in a database). John Taubeneck was also a cofounder (with the author) of the "Wild Donkey Hunts"); Glen Comstock has generously contributed many logging equipment catalogs and vintage logging trade magazines from his extensive collection; Alan B. Armitage, who made the Willamette Loader drawing, and Mark Mogeson of Precision Scale Company, who gave us permission to reproduce it; Steven Gatke, *TimberTimes* co-publisher, contributed many photographs from his collection and assisted with the editing process.

Thanks also to the following: Rolph Hongell, Coos Bay area steam buff; Ken Smejkal and Bill Harkson, who led me to Machine No. 30; Cap Collier, who created the Collier Logging Museum near Chiloquin, Oregon; Robert H. Conner, Southern Oregon steam buff (Robert also has a solution to one of our economic problems: Help fight unemployment - put a steam donkey to work!); Bill McCready, retired machinist, also builder of live steam locomotives and donkeys; Bill Roy, editor and publisher of *Timberbeast*, a logging history periodical; Gordon Smith and Maury Clark, the creators and owners of Camp 18 Logging Museum in Elsie, Oregon. Thanks also to: Bill Ames; Quinn Murk; Mike Boell; Ralph Swan; Chris Horlyck; Lyle Noah; Jim Blain; Ed Kamholz; Bob and Fred Wenzel; Lewis Faught; George Martin; Paul Smith; and Mike Johnson, my son, who cooked for us on our excursions and attracted mosquitoes away from me.

Without diligent editing and design, this book would not have been possible. Philip Schnell, editor and *TimberTimes* co-publisher, is responsible for putting this book together in its present form. He not only edited and designed *In Search of Steam Donkeys*, but also arranged for acquisition of some of the material in the book, and provided scale drawings and some of the text. Not to be forgotten are those who provided editorial assistance: Lynn Sabol, who helped with preliminary typing and proof reading; Debbie Sommer, the midnight manuscript corrector; Diane Gatke, who donated her time and expertise proofreading the manuscript; Susan K. Davis, who did much proofreading, rewriting, and copy editing.

Many old-time loggers gave me further inspiration and encouragement, as well as anecdotes about their lives and work: Homer, Wes, and Granville Simmons; Felix Wilcoxen; Grover Woods; Archie Samuel; Bert Pickens; Chet Anderson; Howard Clark; Howard Stratton; C.E. Van Cise; Rudy Larson; Hershel Phillips; Nellie Chapman; Stanley Mathews; Archie Sailing; and Lionel Youst.

And last, but certainly not least, my heartfelt love and thanks to my wife, Marion, who went to work so that I could complete this book.

This unidentified photograph gives some idea of the difficulties often faced by loggers when moving their equipment from one setting to the next. *Bert Kellogg Collection from Steven Gatke*

INDEX

A

Algoma, Oregon 163
Allegany, Oregon 38
American Hoist & Derrick 71, 74
Amund Ellingson Logging Company 22
Apex Transportation Co. 185
arches, logging with 162
Arlington, Washington 188
Arthur, J.M. 60
Astoria, Oregon 16, 43, 65

B

Baldwin Locomotive Works 65, 212
Bandon, Oregon 154
Barr, R.E. 53
Beaver Creek Logging Co. 138
Beaver Creek, Oregon 138
Beaver Marsh, Oregon 169
Belding, Oregon 182
Bell, Roy C. 266
Bend, Oregon 169, 172
Benson, Simon 134
Benson Timber Co. 61, 102, 120, 121,
    33, 148, 149, 214; Camp Erickson
    59; Camp Tichenor 59; incline 181
Big Creek Logging Co. 198, 234, 239
Big Lagoon 202
Big Lakes Box Co., McGiffert loader 167
big wheels 162
Billy Creek 95
Black Rock, Oregon 57, 98
bleeder valve 29, 43, 46
Blue Ridge, Oregon 20
Blue River, Oregon 73
Bly, Oregon 169
Bohemia Lumber Co. 88
boilers: explosions 26, 52, 63; extended
    firebox 88; lagging, 50, 169; sub-
    merged-head 266
Boise-Cascade Corp. 100
boom 151, 153, 252, 253 (see also
    "loading")
Booth-Kelly Lumber Co. 57, 116, 138, 219
Brady, Washington 193
Bradley Woodard Lumber Co. 155
Bridal Veil Creek 26
Bridal Veil, Oregon 185
Bridal Veil Lumber Company: 22, 26; boiler
    explosion 26: first skyline 127;
    incline 185 (see also Apex Transporta-
    tion Co.)
Brookings Commercial 143
Brookings Lumber Co. 212
Brookings, Oregon 212
Brooks-Scanlon Lumber Co. 164, 171; Bull
    Springs Camp 172
Brown, C. 185
Buckley, Washington 75
Buehner Lumber Company 38
Bureau of Land Management 96
Burns, Al 48
Butte Falls, Oregon 173
Buxton, Oregon 38

C

C.D. Johnson Lumber. Co.: giant simplex
    yarder 103; Mach. No 37 134
cable car system 185
California & Oregon Lumber Co. 212
Camp McGregor 115
Camp 6 Logging Museum, Tacoma Wash. 159
Camp 18 Logging Museum, Elsie, Oregon
    18, 43, 44, 45,
    75, 109, 134, 138, 194
car drum 136
carriage, skidder 225
car-mounted units 159, 219
carriage, slack-line 226
Castle Rock, Washington 54
Chapman, Leslie 96
Chapman Mill on Billy Creek 94
Chapman, Sherman 94
Chiloquin, Oregon 50, 166, 169, 202
"cigar" rafts 120
Clark & Wilson Lumber Co. 18,
    109, 148, 152, 232-233
Clark Creek Logging Co. 211
Clatskanie, Oregon 39, 102, 149, 181
Climax locomotives: 39, 65; "Molly-O" 191
Clyde Equipment Co. of Seattle 75
Clyde Iron Works: skidder 205; track
    layer 164, 193, 202-204 164, 203;
    four-line skidder 205
Coats Driving and Boom Co. 85
Cobbs and Mitchell 103
Cochran, Oregon 103, 230
Coleman, Harry 65
Collier, Cap 164, 166, 203
Collier Logging Museum 50, 156, 167, 202
Columbia & Nehalem River RR 118
Columbia City, Oregon 8
Colvin, Henry 54
compound gearing 78
Connacher Logging Company 87, 138, 150
Consolidated Timber Co. 2, 5, 9, 150, 152
convertible yarder 92, 95, 97
Coos Bay 30, 68, unstable ground of area
Coos Bay Lumber Co. 20, 68; Heisler
    loco 155
Coos Bay Pioneer and Historical Association 20
Coos County 20
Coos County Parks and Recreation 68
Coos Head Pulp Mill 71
Coos River 20, 30
Coquille, Oregon 154
Coquille River 20, 154
Coweeman River 53
Crater Lake, Oregon 165
Creswell, Oregon 28, 29
crotch-line loading 6, 41, 69, 133, 142, 144,
    145, 148, 149, 155, 273
Crown-Willamette, tower skidder 230

D

Dallas, Oregon 98
Daniels Creek 20, 30, 68
Deer Island Logging Co. 119, 145, 211
Delta Park, Portland 134
Detroit, Oregon 267
Diamond Lumber Co. 114

disconnected logging trucks 30
Divide, Oregon 40
Dolbeer donkey: 16, 154; patent draw-
    ings 21,23; patent 20; 17, 19; two-
    cylinder 22
Dolbeer, John 21
Donahue and Kelly 185
donkey drawings 252-263
donkey engine, largest on earth 178
donkey hunts: 71, 84, 85, 90, 100, 182
donkey models 240-251
donkey moving 14, 46, 49, 53, 55, 56, 56,
    58, 76, 80, 265, 277
Dorris, California 165
Douglas County Museum 96
dragsaws 40
Drain, Oregon 96
Duluth, Minnesota 75, 164
"dummy" tree 210
duplex loader 158, 159, 219, 220
Dyche, Bill 127

E

Easter, Jack 106, 114
Ebey Logging Co. 188
Eel Lake 38
Elsie, Oregon 18, 41, 43, 44, 45, 75, 134,
    139, 194
Ericison & Klepp Shipyard 45
Erickson & Son 39
Estacada, Oregon 186
Eugene, Oregon 52, 57, 88, 138
Ewauna Box Co. 162

F

fairleads: double-deck 112
fairleads: roller 40, 102; bullseye 80, 208;
    mainline 80
firewood 198-199
Floyd Lamkin Machinery Company 202
fording a stream 237, 238, 267
Forest Grove, Oregon 51
Forest Lumber Co. 163
Forest Park Committee of Fifty, 18
Forestry Building, Portland, Oregon 18,
    19, 134
Frantz, W.C. "Pete" 57
friction device 38, 242
Flora, Joe 242

G

Gales Creek Logging Co. 44
Garibaldi, Oregon 86; Lions Club 54
General Iron & Steel Works 98
Georgia-Pacific Corp. 134, 138
Gerlinger, George 57
Ginger Creek 115, 147
gin-pole loading 49, 154
Giustina Bros. 143
Glenwood, Oregon 2, 44, 138, 150, 152
Globe Milling Co. 69
Graff, Albert 74
Grays Harbor County 22
Grays Harbor, Washington 56
ground lead yarding 8, 26, 59,67
Gustiss, "Shorty" 42

"guyline" loading 158, 159
gypsy 23
gypsy spool 68

H

Hatfield, Peg 64
haulback line 39
hay-rack boom 116, 140, 141
hay-rack boom loading system 153
heel-boom loading 114, 146
heel-boom loading system 150-152
heel-boom, tree-rigged 147
high-lead 25: logging 77; yarding 8;
    system 105
Himebaugh, C.A. 81
Hongell, Rolph 20, 68, 88
horse logging 162
Hoskins, Oregon 27, 57
Howell, "Billdad" 154
Humboldt County, California 213
Humboldt yarder 8, 80, 81-84, 88, 100-
    102, 106,
Hutchinson Lumber Company 100

I

Idaville, Oregon 5, 86, 191
inclines: 175; incline, counter-balanced 182
incline engines 175; "gypsy" type lowering
    engine 182
Independence, Oregon 211
Insley, Morton 236
interlock 228, 234, 268
International Paper Co. 115, 125

J

J.H. Chambers & Son 155
J.S. Mundy & Co. 45
"jammers" 161
"Japanese skidders" 193
Jewell, Oregon 209
Johnson, Lee 9, 43, 48, 54, 56, 76, 114, 242
Johnson, Robert 48
Jones Boatworks 45

K

Keasey, Oregon 114
Kerriston, Washington 223
Kerry, Albert S. 223
Kerry Line 118
Kerry, Oregon 41, 76
Kerry Timber Co. 76, 112, 220
Kesterson Lumber Co. 165
Kimball Bros. Lumber Co. 143
Kinney, Robert C. Logging Co. 55
Klamath Basin 161
Klamath Falls, Oregon 19, 162, 165, 167,
    168, 202
Knappa, Oregon 234, 239
Knappton Tow Boat Co. 43, 45
Koster Products 112

L

Labbe, John 48, 53

lagging, boilers 50, 169
La Grande, Oregon 212
Lakeside, Oregon 38
Lamm lumber Co. 162
Lane County Museum 138
Larch Mountain 185
Larson, Albin 59, 181
Larson, Rudy 148
Leneve, Oregon 204
Lewis & Clark Exhibition, 1905 134
Lidgerwood: Mach No. 15 60; skidder 223;
    tower skidder 228, 232-233
link and pin couplers 149
loaders: 129-159 tree-rigged 140; heel-
    boom 146, 147, 150; gin-
    pole 49, 154; "guyline" 158-159;
    duplex loader 158-159, 219-220; two-
    tong loading system 158-159
loading jacks 158-159
loading methods 129
loading drum 38, 47
logcars, skeleton 163
Long-Bell: 106; Division of International
    Paper Co. 106, 146, 147, 228
Lorane Valley Lumber Co. 155
lowering engines 175-191; "gypsy"
    type 182, 186; tandem drum
    type 190; Smith & Watson 191
Lulay Brothers Mill 69, 70
Lulay, William, Jr. 69
Lumberman's Memorial Park 54
Lumberton, Oregon 162

M

Mallory Logging Equipment Co. 37, 47, 67
Marcola, Oregon 63
Marschutz and Cantrell 20
Marshfield, Oregon 27, 30
Marshland, Oregon 54, 88
McCloud, California 165
McCloud River Lumber Co. 165
McDonald and Vaughn 20, 30
McDonald, Jack 20
McGiffert loaders 160-173
Medford Corp. 173
Meserve Brothers 56
Modoc Point, Oregon 162
Mohawk River 63
Moore Mill & Lumber Co. 204
Mount Emily Lumber Co., last logs on last
    train 212
moving donkey 14, 49, 51, 53, 55-58, 76,
    80, 124-126, 237-239, 264, 267, 277
Mundy donkey 25, 27, 48, 185
Mundy incline engine 185

N

National Iron Works 20
Neah Bay, Washington 222, 230
Nehalem Timber & Logging Co 87, 107, 113,
    137, 157
Nelson, Gus 48
Newman & Svoboda 109
Newberg, Oregon 51
Newman, Henry J. 109
North Bend, Oregon 20, 38, 271
"North Bend" yarding system 79, 144, 148

Northwest Lumber Company 223
Noyse-Holland Logging Co. 118

O

O.K. Creek 54
O.P. & E. Railway. 138
O.R.&N. Raiway 30
Oak Point, Washington 43
oil burners, automatic 194-195
Oregon-American Lumber Co.: Camp
    Olsen 146, 147; Camp Olsen/Green
    Mountain 80, 101, 115, 146, 228, 229;
    crotch-line loading 146; Ginger Creek
    114,115, 147; moving donkey 80, 101
Overholzer, George & Frank 72

P

Pacific Car & Foundry, "unit" car 219
Pacific Lumber Co. 22, 126
Pacific Maritime Museum 43, 45
Pacific Spruce Corp. 134
Pacific University 51
Palmer & Owen 41
Palmer Lumber Company 65, 185
Palmer Mill 26
Palmer, Oregon 185
Palmerton Lumber Co. 167
parbuckling logs 16, 129
Pelican Bay Lumber Co. 163, 165, 168
Peninsula Lumber Co. 8
Peterson, J.H. "Jack" 48
Peterson Logging Co. 48
Phillips, Hershel 94, 96
Phillips, Nellie (Chapman) 94, 96
Phoenix Logging Co. 202
Pierce, Emmet 20
pile driver 204
Pine Ridge, Oregon 161
Pioneer Logging Museum, Portland, Oregon
    134
piston valves 38
Porter-Carstens Logging Co. 186
Potter, Claude and Alden 62
Powers, Oregon 68, 184
Prosper Mill Co. 154
pumps, water 200-201
Puget Sound Iron & Steel Works 38; duplex
    loaders 159

Q

Quincy, Oregon 39

R

Rainier, Oregon 9, 39,
    43, 45, 46, 48, 66, 176
receding drum 226
Reedsport, Oregon 81, 122
reload, truck-to-railroad 172
Rieger family: Joe 32; Ned 32
rigging diagrams 21, 69, 75, 79, 105, 131,
    133, 151, 153, 159, 171, 210, 224-227,
    271-273
Ritter Creek 27
River Mill, Oregon 63
road engines; 25, 30, 39, 67

rollway 49, 129
roosters, between disconnects 66
Roseburg, Oregon 92
Ruch, Oregon 42

S

S & L Chapman Brothers 73, 94-96
Salmonberry River 85, 182
Samuel, Archie 236
San Diego, California 120
San Francisco, California 20
Scapoose, Oregon 87, 107, 109, 113, 137
Schafer Brothers Logging Co. 193
Scotia, California 103, 126
Seaside, Oregon 55
Seattle Car & Foundry, moving car 101
Seattle, Washington 63
Sedro-Wooley, Washington: duplex loader on
    display 159
Sessom's lowering system 188-189
Sevenmile Creek 154
Shay locomotive 27, 168, 204, 211
Shelton, Washington 73
Shevlin-Hixon Co. 205
Silver Falls Timber Co. 265
Silverton, Oregon 265
Simmons Bros. Logging Co. 197
Simmons Creek 40
Simmons family: Granville 34, 40; Homer
    34; Wes 34
simple-geared yarders 106
Simpson, Dave 27
Simpson Lumber Co 30
Simpson Timber Co 20, 57
"sinkers" 211
Sisters, Oregon 172
Skamokawa, Washington 266
Skelley, Oregon 95, 97
skidder, interlocking 228, 234, 268
skidder logging: 224; skidding drum 224;
    two-speed 230
skyline: 226; skyline drum 226; two-speed
    230; first use 127
slack-line logging: system 131, 226
"sledge hammer" two-speeds 92
sleds, donkey 206-209, 263
slewing engine 75
"slide back" loader 164, 212
Smith & Watson Iron Works: 42, 78, 92, 94-
    96, 98-99, 122, 159; oil burning
    equipment 195, 122
Smith, Alfred E. 98
Smith, Arthur 26, 29
Smith, Gordon 18, 41, 109
Smith, Jim 43
Smith, Paul 241, 243
Smith, T.H. 185
Smith Tug & Barge 43, 45
Smith-Powers Logging Co. 27, 129, 155, 206;
    incline at Camp 6 184
smoke box (or bonnet) 15, 255
snubbers see incline engines
Sowa, Martin 94
spar tree: raising 210; breaking 148;
    jumping 209

spark arrestor 40, 99, 196
Spaulding Logging Co. 27
spool donkey 20
spool tender 23
Sprague River, Oregon 163
spring pole 40, 76, 116
Springfield, Oregon 57, 63, 138
Spruce Production Div., U.S. Army 206
Southern Pacific, Tillamook Branch 85, 182
"squirrel chunk" 150
St. Helens, Oregon 8
steam dummies 65, 66
Stella, Washington 43
strawline drum 38, 47, 68, 226
street railways (dummies) 65, 66
Sturtevant & Craine 154
Sutherlin, Oregon 52
Swede Town 148, 181
swing donkies 67

T

Tacoma, Washington 159
"Tacomas": engines 31, 47, 50; yarder 73,
    104; "old Betts" 96
tail-tree 226
tandem drum road engine 67, 68
tank, water/fuel for yarder 107, 195, 207,
    220
Tatum and Bowen 45
Tenmile Lake 38
Terry, George 20
Tidewater Timber Co. 209
tight sky-line 224, 225, 271, 272
Tillamook Air Base 34
Tillamook County 40
Tillamook County Pioneer Museum 36
Tillamook Forest 84
Tillamook, Oregon 31, 34, 114
"Tommy Moore" block 62
torpedoes, oil 194
tractors, use in logging 162
Transportation and Logging Museum, Portland,
    Oregon 19
Trask River 114
Trullinger, J.C. 16
Tucker, Cliff 81
two-speed yarders: compound geared 219;
    Willamette compound 107-114 "sledge
    hammer" 92; "universal yarding engine
    - two speed" 92-93; 2-speed yard-
    ing 106
two-tong loading system 158-159

U

units, car-mounted 219-220
"universal yarding engine - two speed" 92
unloading donkeys 211

V

Valley & Siletz RR 211
Valsetz, Oregon 103
Vance, John Lumber Co. 22
Van Cise, C.E. (Van) 154

Vaughn, William 20
Vernonia, Oregon 33, 87, 106, 146, 228, 232
vertical spool donkeys 17
Vulcan Iron Works 63

W

Walluski River 16, 65
Washington Iron Works: 28, 40, 41, 52, 71,
    72; compound yarder 90; 12x14
    lowering engine 182-183; 13x18
    yarder 103; 9-1/4 x 13 wide face
    yarder 40; duplex loader 159; tower
    skidder 228
Washington Pulp and Paper, Neah bay,
    Washington 222, 230
Wendling, Oregon 57, 116, 117, 219
West Coast Lumberman 69, 70
West Oregon Lumber Co. 85, 182, 183, 191
West Rainier, Oregon 45
Western Logging Co. 103
Western Lumber Co. 153
Westfir, Oregon 153
Weyerhaeuser Timber Co. 162, 163, 165,
    167-169, 202-203
Wheeler, C.H. Lumber Co.: skidder 103;
    13x14 skidder 230
Whitney Company, The 5, 86, 183, 191
wide face donkeys 25, 27, 42, 63, 267
Wilcoxen, Felix 116
Wilkenson Quarry 75
Willamette Iron & Steel Works:
    boiler replacement 42; car-mounted
    units 220; compound gearing 77;
    Clyde Equip. Co., affiliation with
    Willamette 202; compound geared
    two-speeds 87, 106, 107, 106-116;
    direct-geared two-speed 118; donkey
    erecting floor 10; duplex loaders 158-
    159; Humboldt yarder 8, 76, 80, 81,
    100-102, 106; interlocking skid-
    der 103; tower skidder 228; model
    donkeys 241; road engines 38, 46, 67,
    68, 206, 267; sled design 207; standard
    yarder 52; three-drum loader 130,
    159; two-speed tree-rigged skid-
    der 230; Yeon & Pelton incline 178
Willamette Valley Lumber Co. 57, 98
Willamette-Clyde 203
Winchester Bay Lumber Co. 81, 122
Winchester Creek 122
Wisconsin Logging and Timber Co. 43, 175
Withrow, Ira 266

Y

yarding, ground lead 21
Yeon & Pelton 65, 66
Yeon & Pelton Incline 176; engine 177-178
Yeon John 65
Yoncalla, Oregon 73, 95, 96
Youngs River 65
Yunker & Wiecks Logging Co. 236